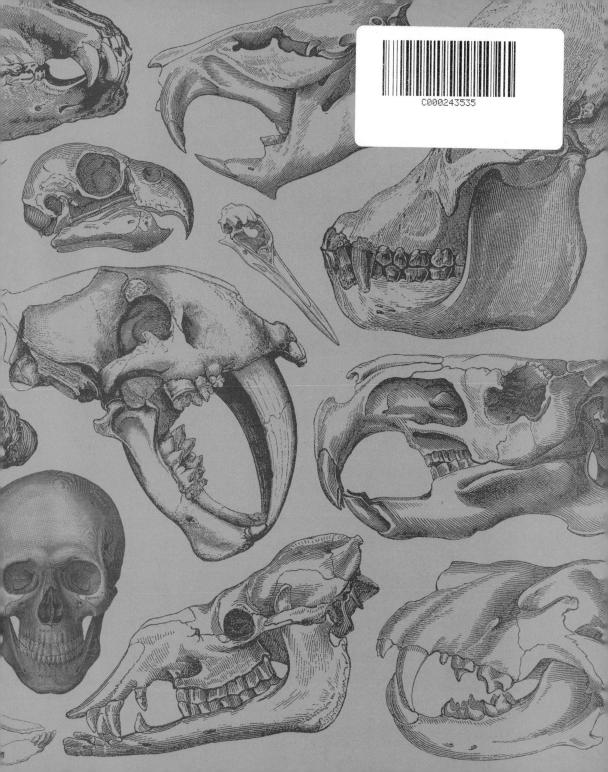

SKELETONS

SKELETONS

THE EXTRAORDINARY FORM & FUNCTION OF BONES

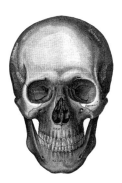

ANDREW KIRK

IVY PRESS

First published in the UK in 2016 by
Ivy Press
210 High Street
Lewes
East Sussex BN7 2NS
United Kingdom
www.ivypress.co.uk

British Library Cataloguing-in-Publication Data
A catalogue record for this book is available from
the British Library

ISBN: 978-1-78240-402-6

This book was conceived, designed, and produced by
Ivy Press
Publisher *Susan Kelly*
Creative Director *Michael Whitehead*
Editorial Director *Tom Kitch*
Commissioning Editor *Sophie Collins*
Art Director *James Lawrence*
Project Editor *Joanna Bentley*
Designer *Emily Portnoi*
Picture Researcher *Katie Greenwood*

Printed in China

10 9 8 7 6 5 4 3 2 1

Andrew Kirk was educated at Oxford
University and worked in publishing for
over twenty years before becoming a
writer. His previous titles have included
books on ancient history and a study of
Thoreau. This is his sixth book.

CONTENTS

INTRODUCTION

Imagine being asked to design a
machine that could turn on a faucet,
fill a balloon with water, run up three
flights of stairs carrying the balloon
without bursting it, open a window,
and then throw the balloon out of the
window so that it made a pleasing splat
on the ground below. You would have
to take account of all the separate
actions involved in this process, and
figure out how to articulate the
structure of your machine so that
it could move smoothly from one
function to the next. Or you could
just do the balloon trick yourself,
because nature has figured all of this
out for you. And the basis of nature's
clever balloon-throwing machine is
the skeleton.

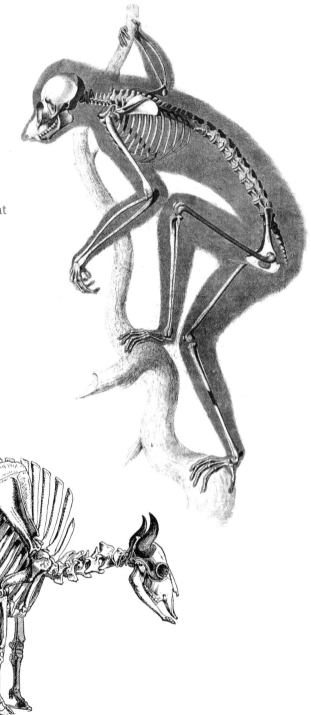

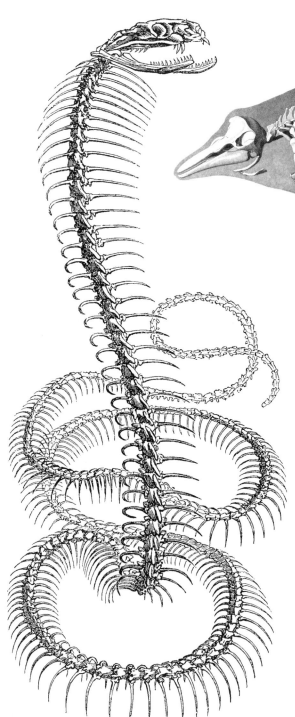

The skeleton is a complex framework of columns, beams, boxes, platforms, and levers, and gives structure not only to the human body but also to the bodies of more than 60,000 other animal species. The same design has been adapted over millions of years by the demands of different habitats and ecological niches to produce animals of all shapes and sizes. Anatomists began to build up an accurate picture of the human skeleton at the beginning of the sixteenth century, and some of the most detailed illustrations of the skeleton were produced by the artist and polymath Leonardo da Vinci. But unless we happen to have an accident that requires an X-ray, this amazing structure remains largely invisible to us.

Most people's first experience of skeletons comes from a trip to the museum and its displays of huge prehistoric dinosaur bones. The remains of these ancient animals were first collected and studied in detail in the nineteenth century. In 1822 Gideon Mantell, an English anatomist and doctor with an interest in collecting fossils, discovered some fossilized teeth in the chalk downlands near his home in Sussex. Mantell's researches led him to the conclusion that these teeth had belonged to a kind of iguana, but one that was at least 60 feet (18 m) long. Although his suggestions initially met with ridicule, further finds confirmed that he had discovered the remains of a giant land-based reptile, Iguanadon. Mantell is now recognized as one of the founders of paleontology, the scientific study of the remains of ancient animals.

As the theories of Charles Darwin regarding evolution came to be widely accepted, so there was an eagerness not only to ascertain the form of individual animals, but also their relationships to each other. The narrative of how animal life had developed over millions of years was gradually pieced together, and it is a narrative based largely on bones.

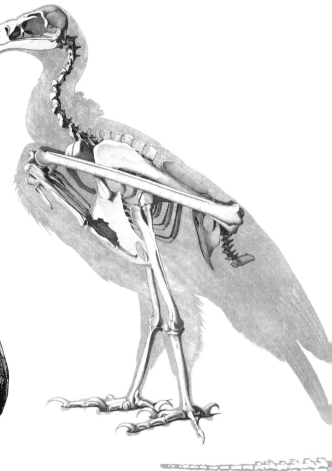

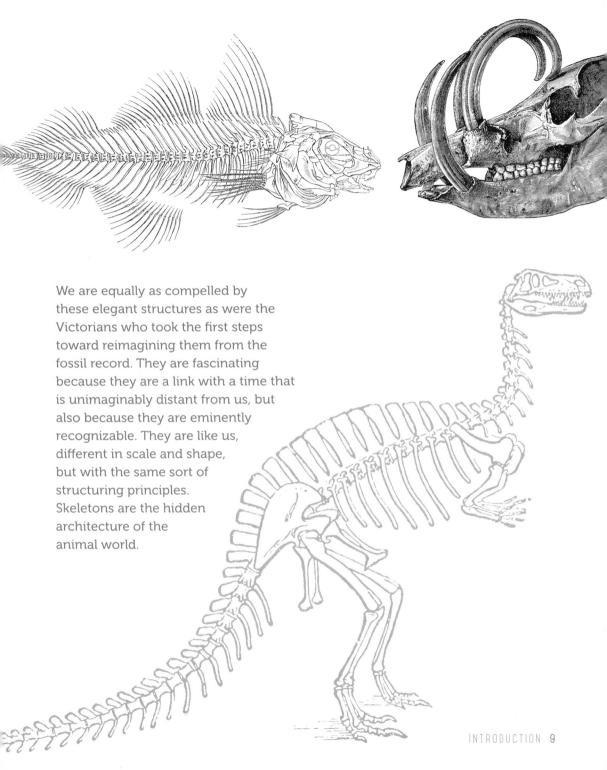

We are equally as compelled by
these elegant structures as were the
Victorians who took the first steps
toward reimagining them from the
fossil record. They are fascinating
because they are a link with a time that
is unimaginably distant from us, but
also because they are eminently
recognizable. They are like us,
different in scale and shape,
but with the same sort of
structuring principles.
Skeletons are the hidden
architecture of the
animal world.

WHAT ARE BONES?

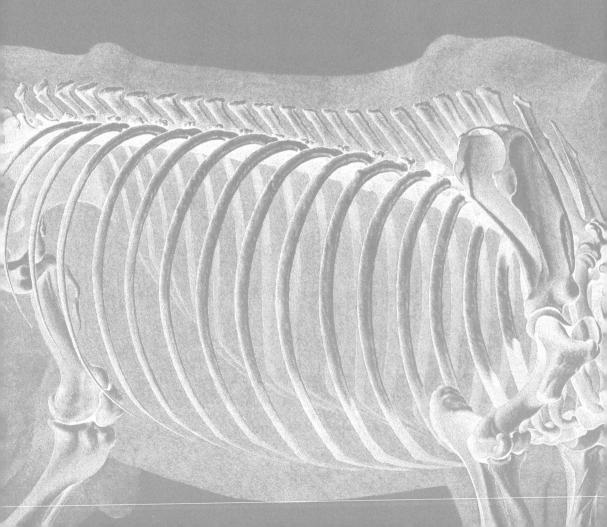

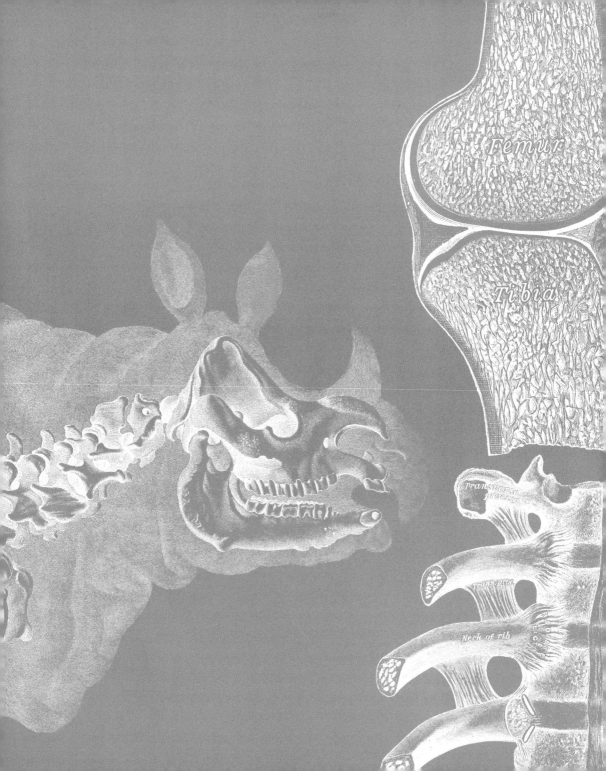

NATURE'S BUILDING MATERIAL

As an engineering and construction material, bone is pretty hard to beat. Being a living material, it has the capacity to grow and therefore to develop into a variety of different shapes and sizes. This makes it an amazingly adaptable and versatile building block.

The earliest evidence of bony structures is in the form of fossilized fish scales from the late Cambrian period, 500 million years ago. From these beginnings evolved the sophisticated range of skeletal structures that we know today.

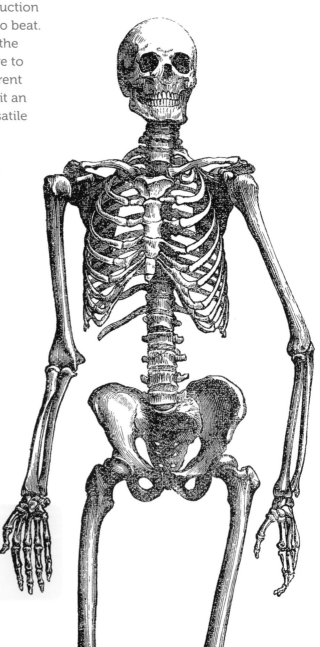

The human skeleton is a complicated arrangement of levers, columns, and hinges that allows a wide range of movements.

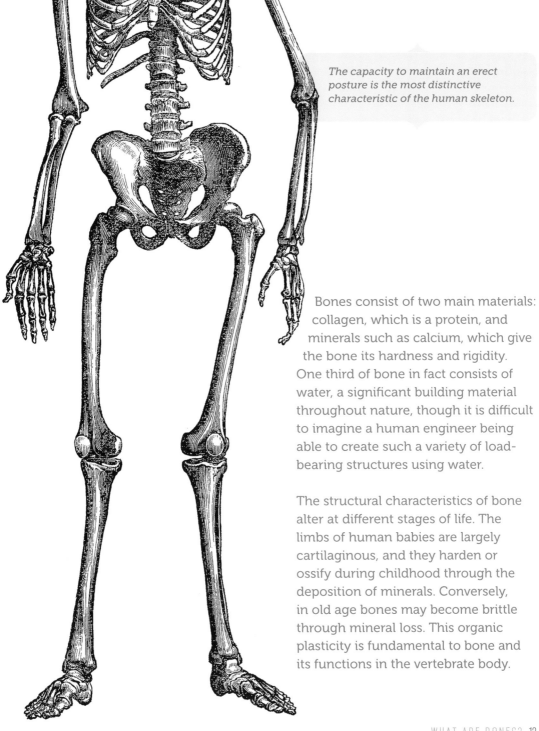

The capacity to maintain an erect posture is the most distinctive characteristic of the human skeleton.

Bones consist of two main materials: collagen, which is a protein, and minerals such as calcium, which give the bone its hardness and rigidity. One third of bone in fact consists of water, a significant building material throughout nature, though it is difficult to imagine a human engineer being able to create such a variety of load-bearing structures using water.

The structural characteristics of bone alter at different stages of life. The limbs of human babies are largely cartilaginous, and they harden or ossify during childhood through the deposition of minerals. Conversely, in old age bones may become brittle through mineral loss. This organic plasticity is fundamental to bone and its functions in the vertebrate body.

INSIDE A BONE

Most types of bone have a similar physical structure. There is an outer casing of hard, solid, compact bone which creates a firm surface called the periosteum, to which the muscles, ligaments, and tendons of the body can attach. This casing layer can be thicker or thinner depending on the stresses to which the particular bone is subject.

Within this casing is the spongy bone, which has a coral-like internal structure that gives it rigidity. This part of the bone contains the jelly-like marrow, which produces red blood cells, and it also holds reserves of important minerals and fatty acids, as well as absorbing toxic elements from the body. The cell structures of bone allow the transfer of nutrients, waste products, and minerals back and forth between the skeleton and the rest of the body, so that there is a constant flux in response to the requirements of the organism overall.

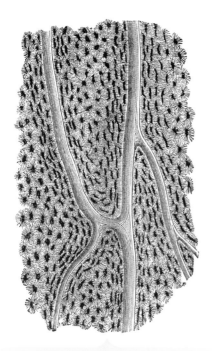

Haversian canals are tiny tubes that run through the outer casing of the bone and carry blood vessels and nerve fibers.

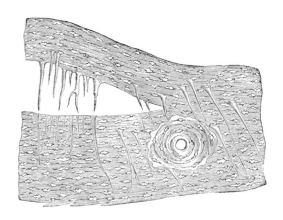

The Haversian canals are formed of thin plates made up of fibers of bony tissue.

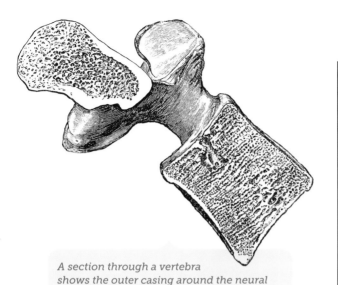

A section through a vertebra shows the outer casing around the neural arch that protects the spinal cord.

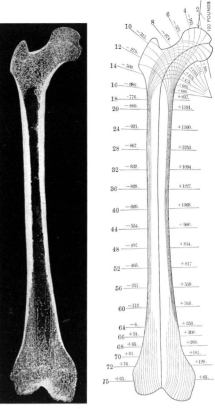

Bone is therefore more than simply an architectural construction material, able to provide a supportive framework that allows for different shapes and sizes and actions of animal bodies; it is central to the functioning of the organism. And as a living material, bone is also capable of repairing itself if it is cracked or broken, generating new material to bridge the gap created by the fracture and restoring the original function.

A section through the head of the humerus showing the interior spongy bone.

A VERSATILE MATERIAL

Bones come in an extraordinary range of shapes and sizes. The thigh bone or femur can be as short as 1½ inches (4 cm) in a hedgehog or as long as 21 inches (53.5 cm) in a giraffe. In the human body alone, bones range in size from the femur, about 17 inches (43 cm) long in the average man, to the stapes, a stirrup-shaped bone in the ear that is about ⅛ inch (0.3 cm) long. Bone is light, strong, and hard. It is resistant to pressure, though less so to twisting or extension. It can form different kinds of linkages, or joints, so that bony structures can bend, rotate, and move from side to side. It can form broad flat plates (like concrete) or long slim struts (like aluminum), load-bearing members (like steel) or hollow boxes (like plastic).

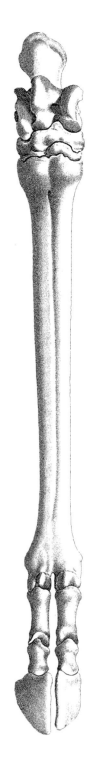

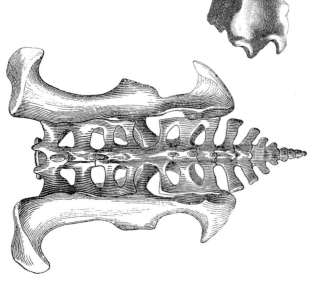

The adaptability of bone as a construction material can be seen throughout the animal kingdom. Skulls can be long and thin, like that of an echidna, or short and broad, like that of an orangutan, heavy and robust, like that of a tiger, or delicate and light, like that of a swallow. Bone can form a relatively simple and straight rod, like a radius or femur, or a complex and convoluted structure with numerous spurs and processes for the attachment of different muscles. All the struts, plates, blocks, joints, and boxes required to create every animal body shape on earth can be produced from this single source material.

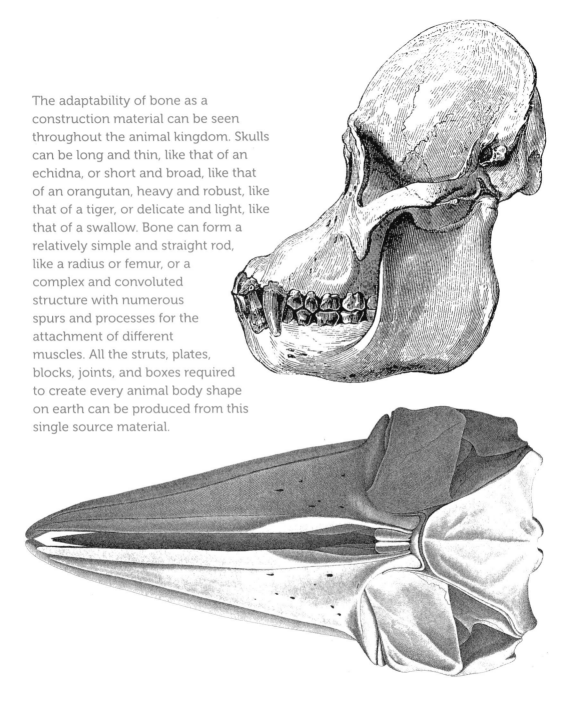

THE SKULL

The skull performs a number of important roles. Although it is a solid bony case, it is made up of several different bones, about 30 in humans, which knit together with fibrous tissue over time. The skull of a human infant has six soft spots in the casing, called fontanels, where the bone has not yet solidified. On an adult skull the position of these joins can be seen.

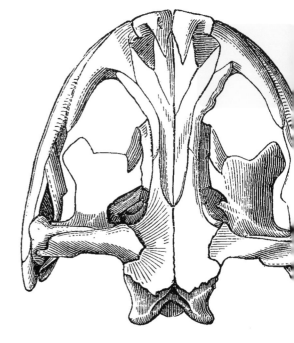

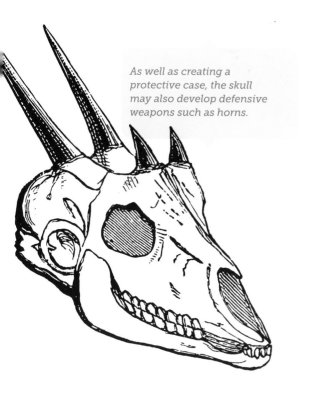

As well as creating a protective case, the skull may also develop defensive weapons such as horns.

The skull holds the brain, which coordinates and controls the body's responses to the environment. The size of the skull gives some indication of an animal's brain size, with the domed forehead of the human skull indicating the well-developed cerebral cortex, associated with reasoning and abstract thought.

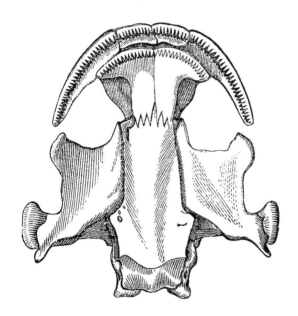

The upper (left) and lower (below) parts of the skull of a salamander show the various separate bones of which it is composed.

The skull carries the eyes, ears, nose, and mouth, which receive information from the outside world for the brain to interpret. These delicate organs are encased in solid bony structures that protect them from shocks and impact. The skull is prominently located and attached to the flexible spine so that it can be readily maneuvered to pick up signals from the animal's surroundings.

The skull is also the route by which nutrients in the form of food and oxygen enter the body, with the jaws gathering and chewing the specific type of food that the animal eats. Within this basic framework animal skulls display a range of different shapes and proportions, depending on where the animal lives, how it moves, and what it eats (and whether it needs to avoid being eaten).

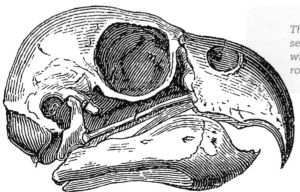

The skull houses and protects the sense organs—eyes, ears, and nose— which in some animals take up more room than the brain.

APPENDICULAR BONES

The appendicular bones are the bones of the four limbs. They follow a general pattern of one upper bone connected by a joint to two lower bones. In most mammals and reptiles these are relatively long and thin bones, though there are exceptions, such as the humerus of a mole, which looks nothing like what you might expect.

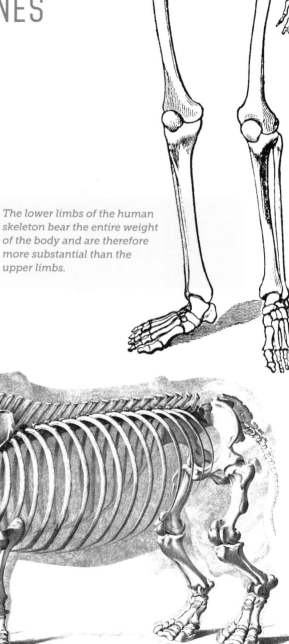

The lower limbs of the human skeleton bear the entire weight of the body and are therefore more substantial than the upper limbs.

The appendicular bones of the rhinoceros are robust supportive columns, reflecting the animal's bulk.

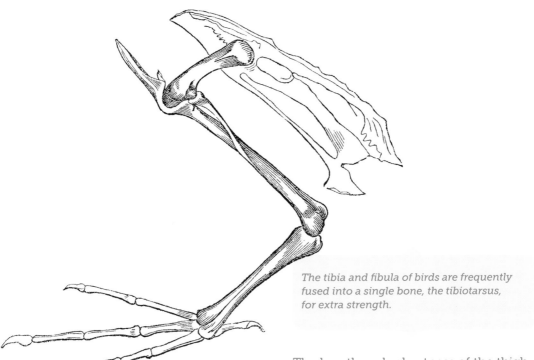

The tibia and fibula of birds are frequently fused into a single bone, the tibiotarsus, for extra strength.

The femur or thigh bone is the longest bone in the human body, and is usually considered to be one of the strongest, supporting as it does the weight of the body and offering attachment points for the muscles that control the hip and knee joints. The ratio of the femur length to the entire body is more or less constant across both sexes and in all ethnic groups, making up roughly one quarter of a person's height.

The length and robustness of the thigh bone gives a good idea of the size of an animal and its method of locomotion. The thigh bone of a cat or a gazelle is quite slender relative to its length, reflecting the fact that these animals are fast-moving. The thigh bone of a cow or a rhinoceros is much more thick and stout. The thigh bone of an elephant, like all its leg bones, lacks the marrow cavity common to most bony structures. Instead the inside of the bone consists of a network of densely packed spongy cavities which make the leg much stronger than it would otherwise be.

THE PELVIS

The hip bones, or the pelvic girdle, attach the hind legs of an animal to its spine and transmit the push of the back legs to the rest of the body when it moves. The basic shape is the same, with a blade at the top of the hip bone called the ilium, a socket for the thigh bone, and a curved plate at the bottom called the ischium, which connects with the ischium on the corresponding hip bone on the other side of the animal.

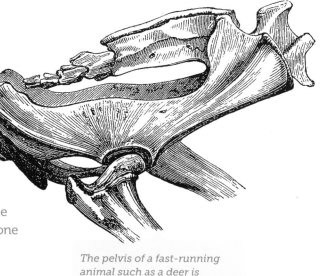

The pelvis of a fast-running animal such as a deer is usually narrow and elongated.

The arrangement of the crocodile's pelvis relative to the spine means that its legs stick out sideways rather than downward from its body.

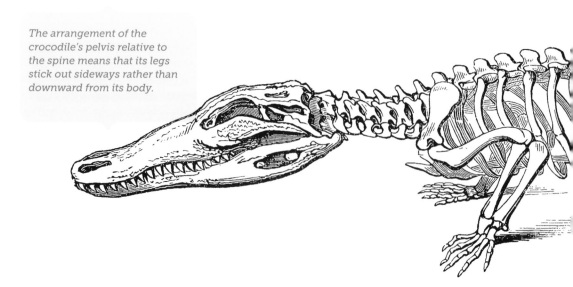

The pelvis of a heavy and slow-moving animal such as an elephant is rounded, with broad ilial plates for the attachment of large muscles.

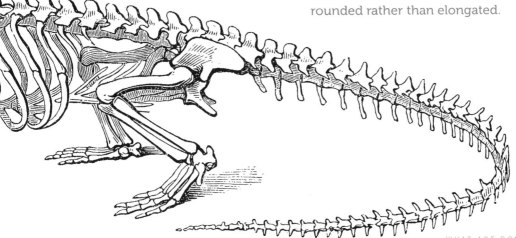

The elongation of the pelvis reflects the way the animal moves. The ilia of a cow's pelvis are broad, to give a wide surface area for the big muscles that are required to move the heavy animal around. The pelvis of a deer or an antelope has long ilial blades, effectively extending the length of their hind legs for fast running. Their pelvises can also pivot to some extent on the spine, giving greater leverage.

An animal that walks on four legs will have its pelvis more or less at right angles to the spine; in some animals, like the crocodile, the pelvis is actually fused at right angles to the spine. By contrast the human pelvis is in a straight line with the spine so as to balance the body weight directly above the feet, and the pelvis is broad and rounded rather than elongated.

THE SCAPULA

The rear legs of most four-legged animals are used for moving it around, whether running, walking, or jumping. The front legs, however, perform different tasks for different animals, or even different tasks for the same animal, so that the forelimbs of a chimpanzee, for example, are sometimes legs and sometimes arms. The key to this adaptability is the scapula or shoulder blade, a triangular bone that connects the forelimbs to the spine and ribs. It can usually tilt to various angles and it has a ball-and-socket joint at the base that allows the upper bone of the forelimb, the humerus, a wide degree of maneuverability.

Shoulder blades or scapulae all have the same more or less triangular shape, with a ridge running from top to bottom.

The variations on the basic scapula shape as seen in, from top to bottom, the rhino, walrus, giraffe, and koala.

24

The triangular shape is also modified in various ways. The shoulder blade of a wolf is long and thin, giving extra extension to its front legs for fast running. The shoulder blade of a walrus is a large squat plate to anchor the front flippers, which it uses for propulsion. The shoulder blades of digging animals like armadillos and moles are similarly broad and large relative to their size. By contrast, a kangaroo has a relatively small shoulder blade since its forelimbs do very little work.

The shoulder blades of birds are made up of two bones, the scapula and the coracoid, which braces the wing against the breastbone. Birds share this feature with reptiles, which has led to suggestions that birds were originally descended from reptiles. The shoulder blade of a bird is characteristically long and thin.

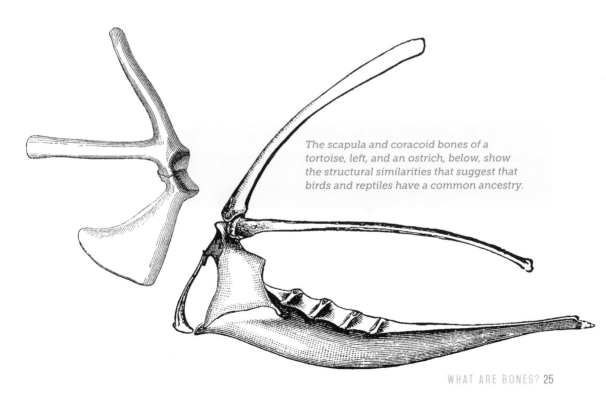

The scapula and coracoid bones of a tortoise, left, and an ostrich, below, show the structural similarities that suggest that birds and reptiles have a common ancestry.

VERTEBRAE

The spine is made up of a set of bones, the vertebrae, which connect in a chain. The number of vertebrae varies from animal to animal—the human spine has 33 vertebrae, the frog's has 9, the elephant's 48, and the python's up to 400.

Each vertebra consists of a rounded central bone, the centrum, with an arch attached to it that carries the spinal cord. This arch has a thick casing of solid bone to protect the delicate nerves that run through it. Bony "wings" called processes project from the centrum for the muscles of the torso to connect to. The spinous process of a human vertebra points downward, but those of four-legged animals point directly upward. In large, heavy animals these spinous processes can be very substantial. Transverse processes project from either side of the vertebra for further muscle attachment. The size and shape of these processes varies according to the physical characteristics of the animal and the way in which it moves.

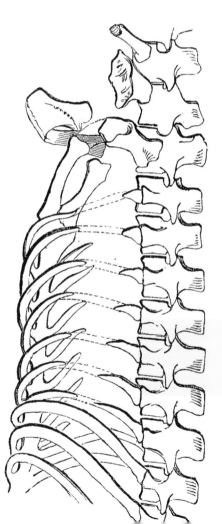

The vertebrae butt up against each other to form a tough but flexible column, seen here in the crocodile's spine.

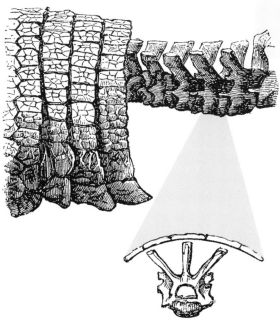

The vertebral processes of the armadillo form an internal support for its arched carapace.

Some vertebrae fuse together to form a single entity, like the human sacrum and coccyx. Birds in particular have two specific fused sections: the synsacrum, where the pelvis attaches to the spine, and the pygostyle, the final fused caudal vertebrae, which gives a solid attachment for the tail feathers that control landing.

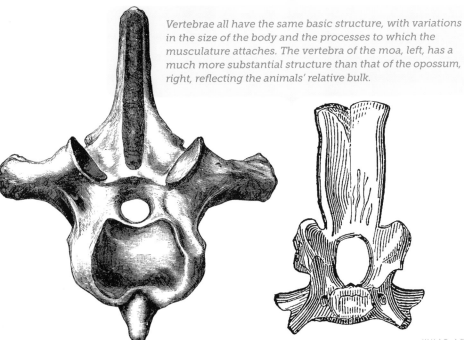

Vertebrae all have the same basic structure, with variations in the size of the body and the processes to which the musculature attaches. The vertebra of the moa, left, has a much more substantial structure than that of the opossum, right, reflecting the animals' relative bulk.

JOINTS

In order for a vertebrate animal to function, its skeleton has to be articulated, that is, the bones need to be able to move relative to each other. This is achieved through joints where separate bones connect, and in mammals there are three types. Fibrous joints, like those in the skull, join the bones tightly together with bands of collagen and don't allow movement. Cartilaginous joints connect bones by means of fibers or pads of collagen which allow a small amount of movement. An example would be the pads between the vertebrae that allow them to move slightly relative to each other.

The third and most common type, as well as being the most useful in terms of mobility, are synovial joints. These consist of a capsule that surrounds the region where two bones meet. The ends of the bones have a layer of cartilage, and the capsule is filled with synovial fluid, which acts as a lubricant to allow the ends of the bones to move smoothly past each other.

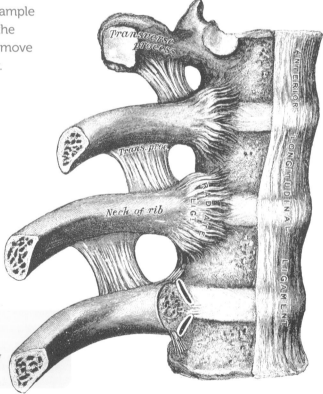

Disks of cartilaginous tissue sit between each vertebra to create flexible, shock-absorbing connections.

Synovial joints take many different forms that enable different kinds of movement. The upper limbs of mammals connect to the body via ball-and-socket joints that allow rotation; the elbows are hinge joints; the two bones of the forelimb have pivot joints so that they can rotate around each other; and the bones of the fingers have condyloid joints, a modified ball and socket which allows the fingers to bend but not rotate. Combinations of these joints in vertebrates create a highly maneuverable structure that can perform many different functions.

This section through the cranium shows one of the fibrous joints that knit the various skull bones together.

The knee joint is a modified hinge between the femur and the tibia, with the patella attached by ligaments to each and the whole contained within a synovial membrane.

JAWS & TEETH

Like the spine, the jaw was a major evolutionary progression in terms of getting our ancestors out of the sea and onto dry land. The first jawless fish could only suck or sieve food, and so would have been highly restricted in terms of diet. The development of jaws and teeth about 450 million years ago greatly enlarged the range of things that an animal could eat, and therefore the range of habitats that it could colonize.

Fish jaws have a complex articulation that gives them a wide gape, and a predator like the gurnard is equipped with small, spikelike teeth.

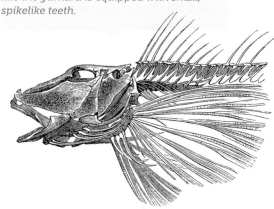

The baboon has strong jaws for cracking nuts, and differentiated teeth reflecting a varied diet.

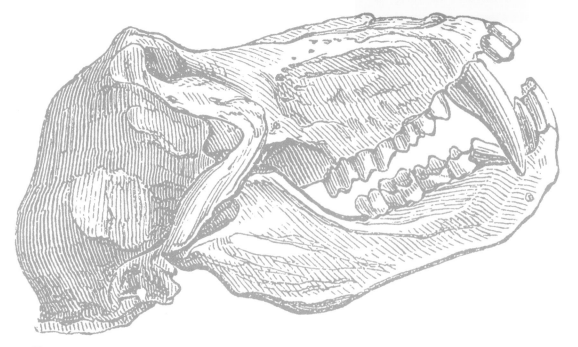

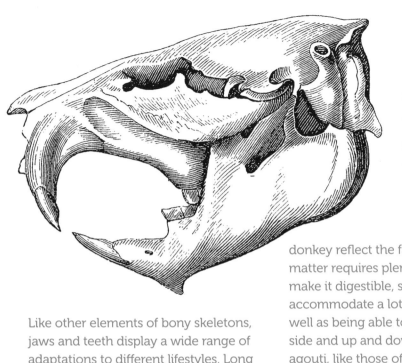

Like other elements of bony skeletons, jaws and teeth display a wide range of adaptations to different lifestyles. Long narrow jaws like those of anteaters are designed for probing into crevices and holes in search of insects, but they are not very strong. The jaws of a large predator such as a lion are relatively short but massive, producing a powerful shearing bite. The long broad jaws of a donkey reflect the fact that vegetable matter requires plenty of chewing to make it digestible, so the jaws need to accommodate a lot of grinding teeth as well as being able to move from side to side and up and down. The jaws of an agouti, like those of other rodents, have large incisors designed for gnawing fibrous plants and cracking nuts. Each variation has developed from the same basic structure.

Like many herbivores, camels lack top incisors, with the lower incisors instead pressing against a tough pad on the upper jaw to rip up plant material.

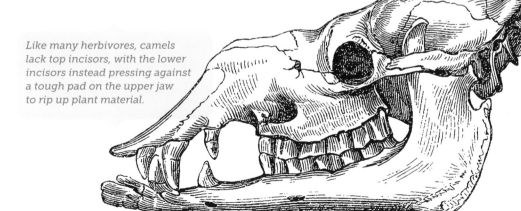

EXOSKELETONS

In numerical terms, animals with bony skeletons only make up a very small proportion of the earth's population. They are vastly outnumbered by the invertebrates—animals such as insects, spiders, and shellfish. These animals have their skeleton on the outside, an exoskeleton, as opposed to the internal skeleton we have looked at so far, the endoskeleton.

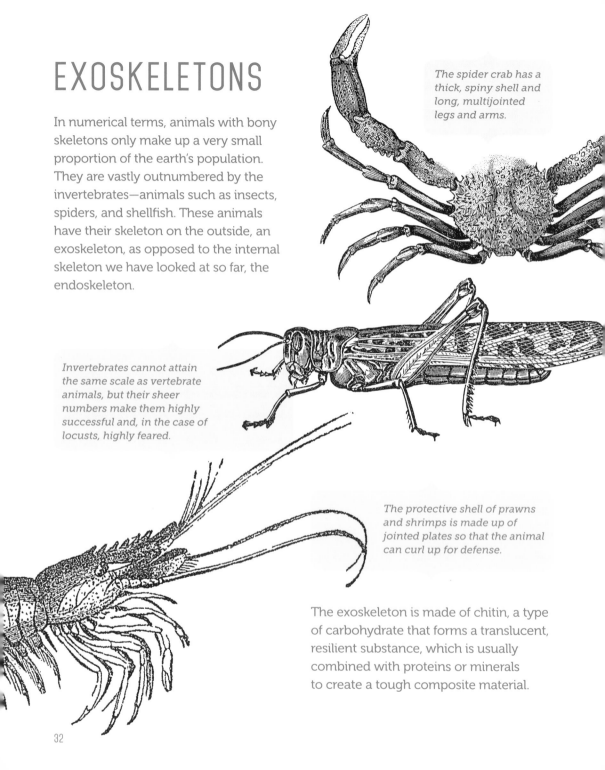

The spider crab has a thick, spiny shell and long, multijointed legs and arms.

Invertebrates cannot attain the same scale as vertebrate animals, but their sheer numbers make them highly successful and, in the case of locusts, highly feared.

The protective shell of prawns and shrimps is made up of jointed plates so that the animal can curl up for defense.

The exoskeleton is made of chitin, a type of carbohydrate that forms a translucent, resilient substance, which is usually combined with proteins or minerals to create a tough composite material.

The sheer numbers of invertebrates indicate that an exoskeleton is a viable adaptation to life on earth, but it does have disadvantages. The skeleton cannot expand, so the developing animal has to shed its outer skeleton in order to grow, which makes it vulnerable. An exoskeleton can only articulate to a limited degree, so mobility is restricted. There is also a limit to the size an animal with an exoskeleton can attain, since above a certain size the exoskeleton will be simply too thick and heavy for the animal's muscles to support. The giant mutant killer ants beloved of sci-fi B-movies would have posed no threat to humans, since they would have collapsed under their own weight.

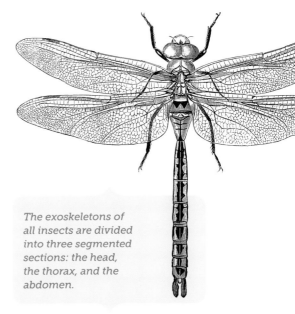

The exoskeletons of all insects are divided into three segmented sections: the head, the thorax, and the abdomen.

Marine invertebrates, which are buoyed up by the surrounding water, can grow bigger to some degree. However, the bony endoskeleton, which takes up a far smaller proportion by mass of the animal's body, permits a much larger body to develop.

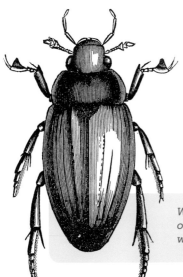

Water beetles can retain pockets of air under their wing cases while they dive underwater.

THE BASIC
SKELETON

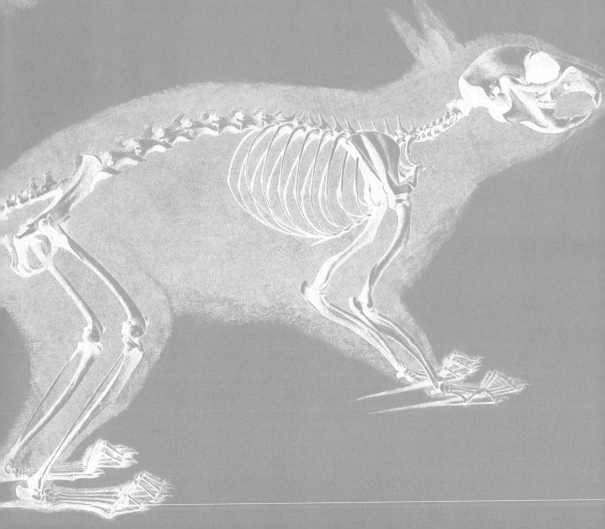

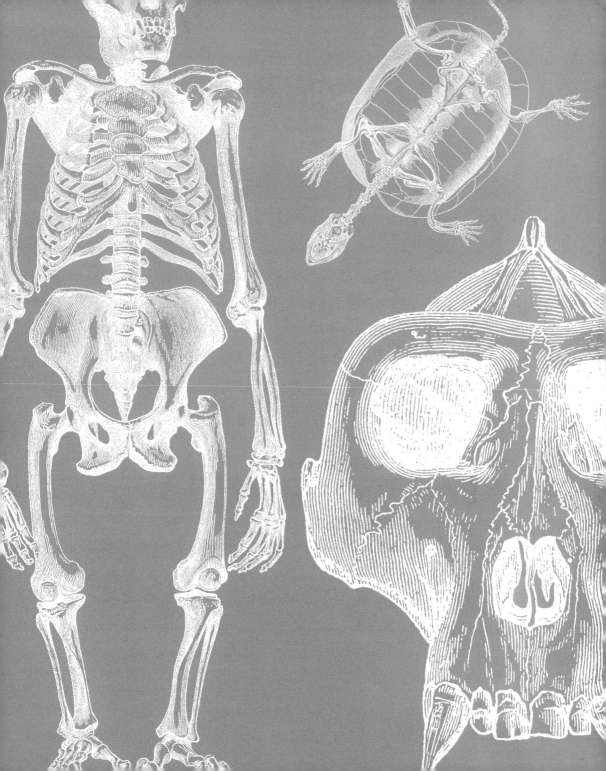

SKELETAL STRUCTURE

These two bony structures show clear similarities. There is a central spine to which all the other sections connect. There is a skull with eye sockets and other orifices and a movable lower jaw equipped with teeth. There is a cage of ribs curving round from the spine to join at the chest of the animal to form a barrel-shaped trunk. There are four legs attached to bony plates at the front and rear of the animal, made up of three jointed sections. And both animals are standing on elongated toes.

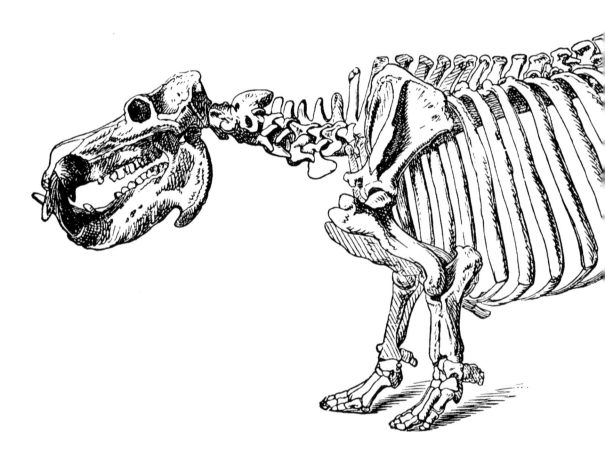

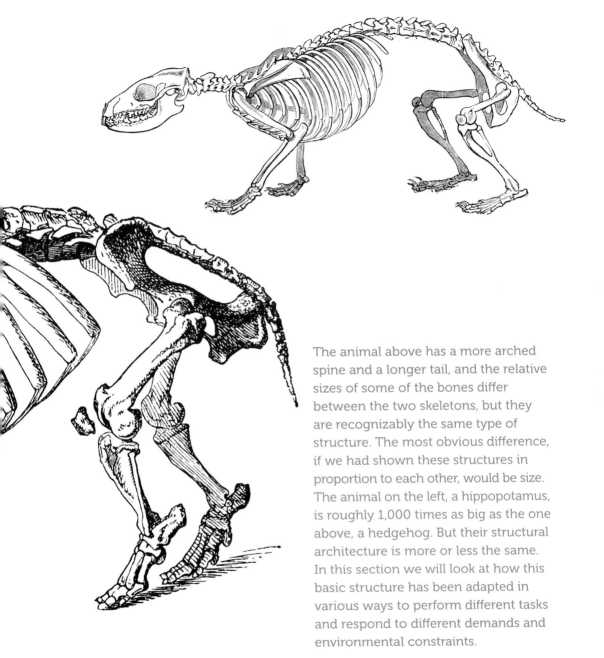

The animal above has a more arched spine and a longer tail, and the relative sizes of some of the bones differ between the two skeletons, but they are recognizably the same type of structure. The most obvious difference, if we had shown these structures in proportion to each other, would be size. The animal on the left, a hippopotamus, is roughly 1,000 times as big as the one above, a hedgehog. But their structural architecture is more or less the same. In this section we will look at how this basic structure has been adapted in various ways to perform different tasks and respond to different demands and environmental constraints.

HUMAN

The skeleton most familiar to us is, of course, our own. It follows the standard pattern of skull, spine, rib cage, and appendicular limbs, but there are two key features that distinguish this skeleton and point to some of the reasons why humans have adapted so successfully to life on earth. The most significant is that, unlike any of the other four-limbed skeletons examined in this book, this one stands on two legs. Some of the other apes can move while upright, but the human skeleton is the only one that is adapted completely for two-legged walking.

The bowl-shaped pelvis, positioned midway up the skeleton, is in line with the spine, so that the torso is balanced directly above the legs. The spine itself is slightly S-shaped, to help align the center of gravity of the head and torso.

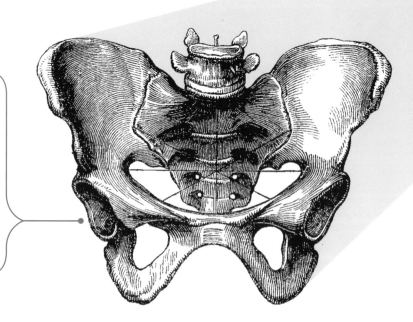

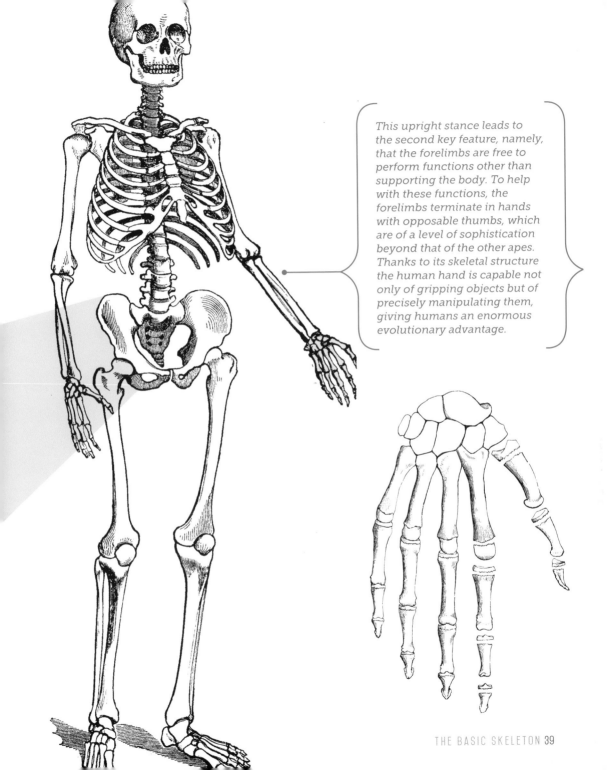

This upright stance leads to the second key feature, namely, that the forelimbs are free to perform functions other than supporting the body. To help with these functions, the forelimbs terminate in hands with opposable thumbs, which are of a level of sophistication beyond that of the other apes. Thanks to its skeletal structure the human hand is capable not only of gripping objects but of precisely manipulating them, giving humans an enormous evolutionary advantage.

HIPPOPOTAMUS

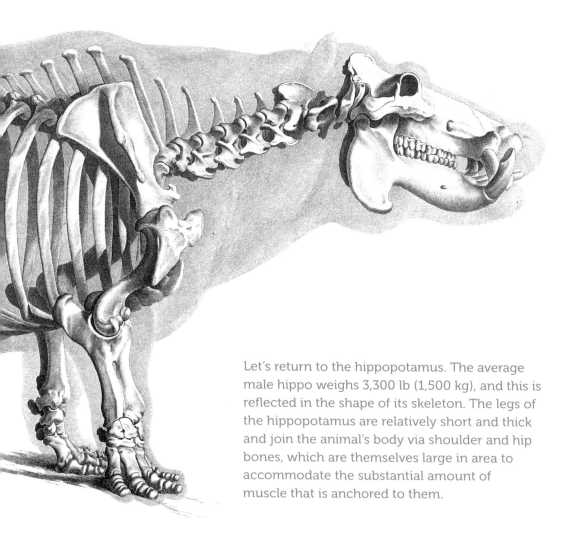

Let's return to the hippopotamus. The average male hippo weighs 3,300 lb (1,500 kg), and this is reflected in the shape of its skeleton. The legs of the hippopotamus are relatively short and thick and join the animal's body via shoulder and hip bones, which are themselves large in area to accommodate the substantial amount of muscle that is anchored to them.

The hippo's semiaquatic lifestyle is reflected in the shape of its skull, which has the nostril and eye sockets located near the top so that the animal can submerge in the water while keeping its nose and eyes above the surface. The hippo's lower jaw is hinged a long way back in its skull, which means it can open its mouth extremely wide and make good use of its huge canines for defense or attack. Hippos are extremely aggressive and dangerous and are rarely preyed upon even by the crocodiles that share their habitat. Those enormous teeth play no part in feeding, since hippos are herbivores, pulling up grass with their lips and grinding it with specialized molars.

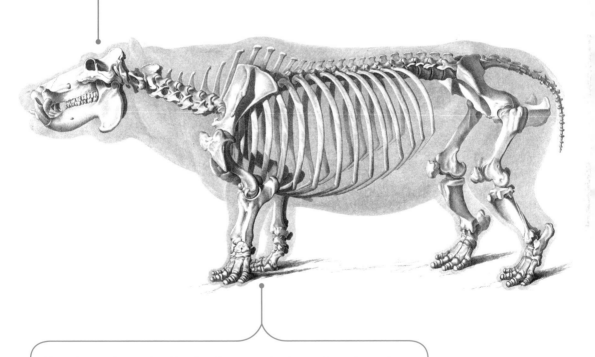

Since it spends much of its time in water, the force of gravity acting on the hippopotamus is not as great as that which affects comparably large animals, such as elephants and rhinos, which live entirely on land. For this reason these animals' legs are bigger relative to their bodies than those of hippos.

SQUIRREL

The skeleton of the hippopotamus is adapted to a life spent largely in water with a relatively small territorial range and a diet of grasses. The skeleton of the squirrel indicates a very different lifestyle and habitat.

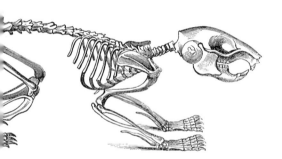

Most species of squirrel are arboreal, and a number of aspects of its skeletal structure reflect this. The leg bones are long and slender to facilitate scampering along branches and jumping from one to another. The squirrel has long sharp claws to help it grip the bark of trees and climb up. Its long and highly flexible tail aids with balancing and acts as a rudder when the animal leaps through the air. Squirrels can rotate the ankles of their rear legs through 180 degrees, which means that they can run down trees head first with their hind feet pointing upward for grip. The entire skeleton is as light as possible to allow for speed and maneuverability.

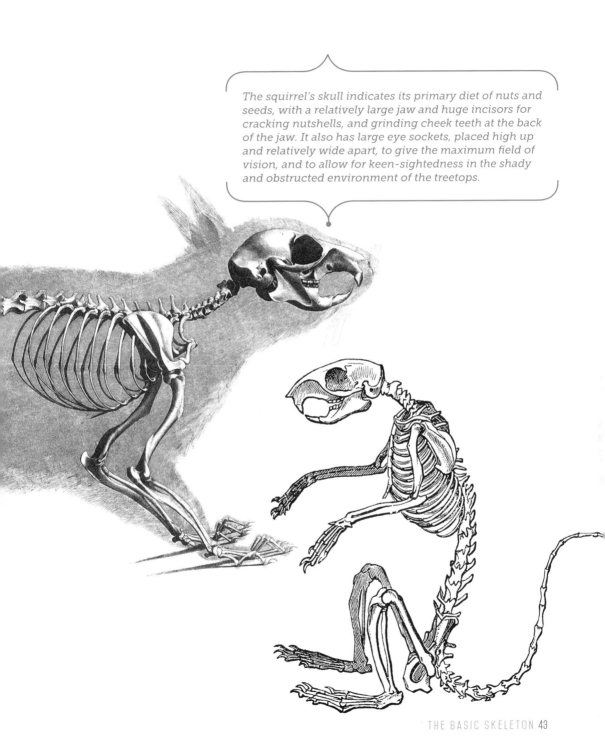

The squirrel's skull indicates its primary diet of nuts and seeds, with a relatively large jaw and huge incisors for cracking nutshells, and grinding cheek teeth at the back of the jaw. It also has large eye sockets, placed high up and relatively wide apart, to give the maximum field of vision, and to allow for keen-sightedness in the shady and obstructed environment of the treetops.

LION

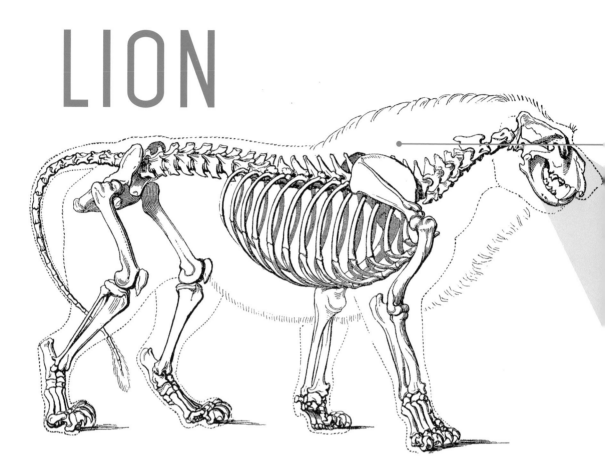

The skeleton of a lion has some distinctive features that offer clues to its lifestyle. The bones of the forelimbs are robust and sturdy, which gives the skeleton a front-heavy appearance. The skeletal pattern of most four-legged animals shows a preponderance of bone mass in the rear limbs, since these do most of the work of propelling the animal along. The lion, however, depends on its immensely strong forelimbs for grasping and wrestling large prey animals to the ground, so the bones of the front and back legs are equally substantial.

The lion's shoulder blade is large to allow for the attachment of the strong muscles that control the forelimbs. The scapula is also set high on the animal's spine, which allows it to creep stealthily along low to the ground with its spine lowered between the front legs when approaching prey. The lion's substantial foreparts cushion the impact of landing when it leaps onto a prey animal, while its claws help it to grip.

Its huge jaws are equipped with long canines, as well as carnassial teeth behind that shear past each other in a slicing motion. The large jaw muscles are anchored to a flange at the back of the skull, producing an immensely powerful biting force. All of these structural elements come together to produce a supremely developed hunter.

MOLE

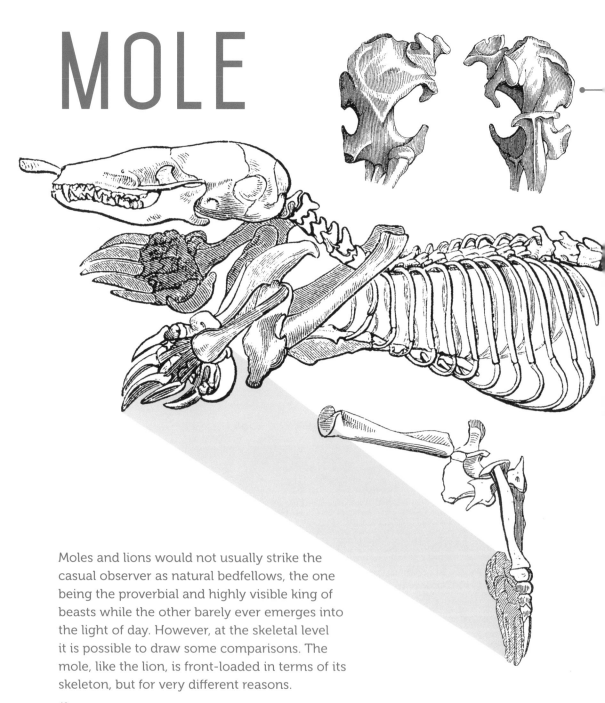

Moles and lions would not usually strike the casual observer as natural bedfellows, the one being the proverbial and highly visible king of beasts while the other barely ever emerges into the light of day. However, at the skeletal level it is possible to draw some comparisons. The mole, like the lion, is front-loaded in terms of its skeleton, but for very different reasons.

The great proportion of the mole's bone mass is made up of its huge forelimbs and feet and the relatively large skull. The mole is a digging machine, and those enormous spatulate forefeet are designed to shift earth quickly and efficiently. The bones that make up the forelimbs are short and stout, and the humerus is quite unlike the long and slim equivalent bone in most four-legged animals, being much more platelike with various points and projections. These provide anchorage points for the musculature that allows the mole to dig so effectively.

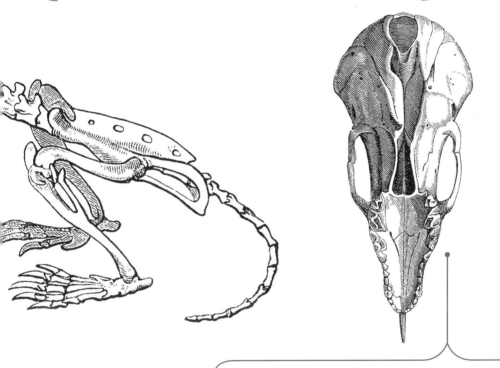

The skull is similarly designed for the mole's unusual environment, being long and pointed at the front to facilitate movement though the earth. The mole has sharp incisors and canines for its diet of worms, but the eye sockets are tiny, since large eyes would be of little use in an environment with no light. And the mole is as effective a hunter below ground as the lion is above.

GORILLA

The gorilla's skeleton is much like our own, though with different proportions. The pelvis is rounded and bowl-like, indicating that this animal can stand on its hind legs, leaving its arms free to perform other tasks. Its hands have opposable thumbs, a characteristic of primates, and so do its feet. And there is no tail, the lack of which is a key identifying feature of apes.

However, there are also clues in the skeleton that indicate differences between a gorilla's habits and lifestyle and those of humans. The pelvis, for instance, is more elongated than a human pelvis, and this together with the long arms indicates that although the gorilla can stand on its hind legs, it walks around on all fours. The gorilla's arms are longer than its legs, but not significantly so, which shows that it is a ground dweller. Arboreal apes, which spend most of their time in trees, have arms that can be as much as 50 percent longer than their legs, since their primary way of getting around is by swinging and leaping from branch to branch.

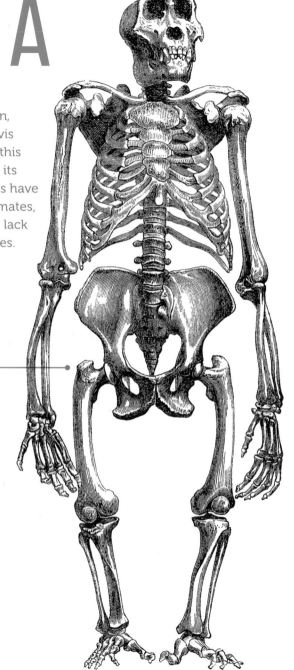

The skull also reflects the gorilla's lifestyle, in this case its diet. The canines are not greatly developed, which shows that the animal is not a meat eater but a herbivore. Another indication of this is the lump on the top of the skull, called the sagittal crest. This anchors the large jaw muscles required to pulp the relatively indigestible plant material that makes up the gorilla's diet.

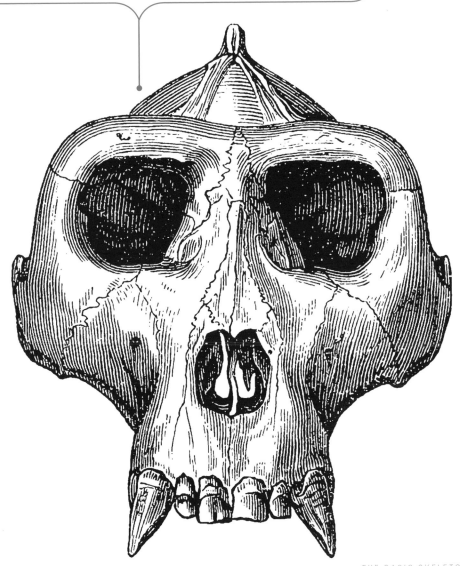

GIRAFFE

The most obvious feature of the giraffe is its long neck, which accounts for over half the length of its spinal column, a much greater proportion than for any of its close relatives. Surprisingly, the neck of a giraffe consists of the same number of vertebrae as our own, seven, although clearly the individual vertebrae are much larger, about 11 inches (28 cm) long. This elongation occurs as the giraffe develops, giraffe calves having shorter necks in proportion to their bodies than adults.

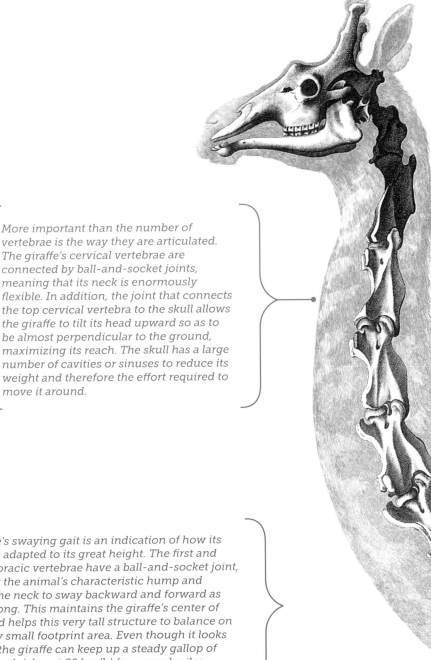

More important than the number of vertebrae is the way they are articulated. The giraffe's cervical vertebrae are connected by ball-and-socket joints, meaning that its neck is enormously flexible. In addition, the joint that connects the top cervical vertebra to the skull allows the giraffe to tilt its head upward so as to be almost perpendicular to the ground, maximizing its reach. The skull has a large number of cavities or sinuses to reduce its weight and therefore the effort required to move it around.

The giraffe's swaying gait is an indication of how its skeleton is adapted to its great height. The first and second thoracic vertebrae have a ball-and-socket joint, producing the animal's characteristic hump and allowing the neck to sway backward and forward as it walks along. This maintains the giraffe's center of gravity and helps this very tall structure to balance on a relatively small footprint area. Even though it looks ungainly, the giraffe can keep up a steady gallop of about 30 mph (almost 50 km/h) for several miles.

SEA LION

Although most mammal species are land-dwelling, there are also aquatic mammals whose skeletons demonstrate the adaptability of bony structures in meeting the demands of different environments.

The sea lion's arms are short and robust to support the weight of the animal when on land. In fact, the sea lion can use both its fore- and rear limbs to walk on land, since its pelvis is slightly tilted relative to its spine. In contrast, a seal's pelvis is directly in line with its spine, so this animal cannot use its rear legs to walk in the same way.

The sea lion's overall body shape shows how the skeleton has adapted to life in the sea, with broad shoulders and a narrow pelvis creating a streamlined profile. The shoulder blade is huge, which suggests that a large attachment area for musculature is required and that the main source of locomotion is the forelimbs, as opposed to the rear as is the case with most mammals. The sea lion's rear limbs are used mostly for steering. The most obvious skeletal development is the hands and feet, which are elongated to create a large surface area of flipper for good propulsion. The hands have claws which give the sea lion some degree of ability to grip and help it to move on land.

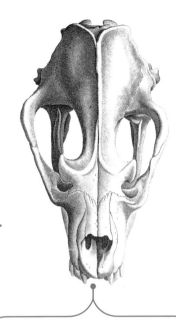

The sea lion is a predator, as is evident from the well-developed canines in its jaw. The skull has large eye orbits, indicating that the animal spends a lot of time in murky waters looking for prey. It is pointed and narrow to offer as little resistance as possible to the water.

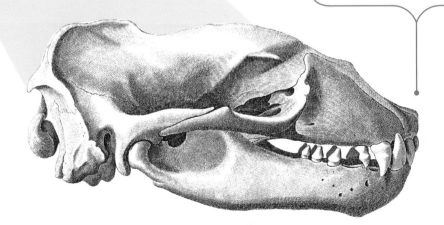

WHALE

The ancestors of modern mammals emerged from the ocean about 350 million years ago. Whales are unusual members of the mammal family inasmuch as their ancestors subsequently returned to the sea, and the 40 species of whales are spread widely across the world's oceans.

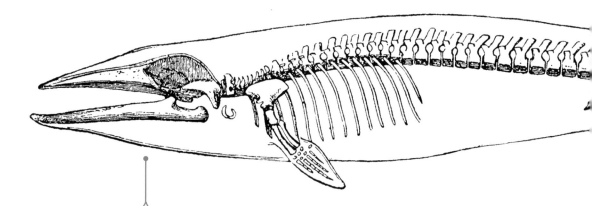

Whales are divided into two broad groups: those with teeth (called Odontocetes), such as sperm whales and dolphins, and those without teeth (Mysticetes), such as hump-backed and gray whales. Mysticetes have large heads and mouths relative to their body size, since they feed by hoovering up huge amounts of water and straining out the minute creatures which are their main food source.

The cervical end of the spine is also designed for efficient movement, with the cervical vertebrae being flattened and fused together to minimize any sideways movement of the head as the animal cuts through the water. The forelimbs are used for steering, with their bones being short and robust compared to those of land mammals.

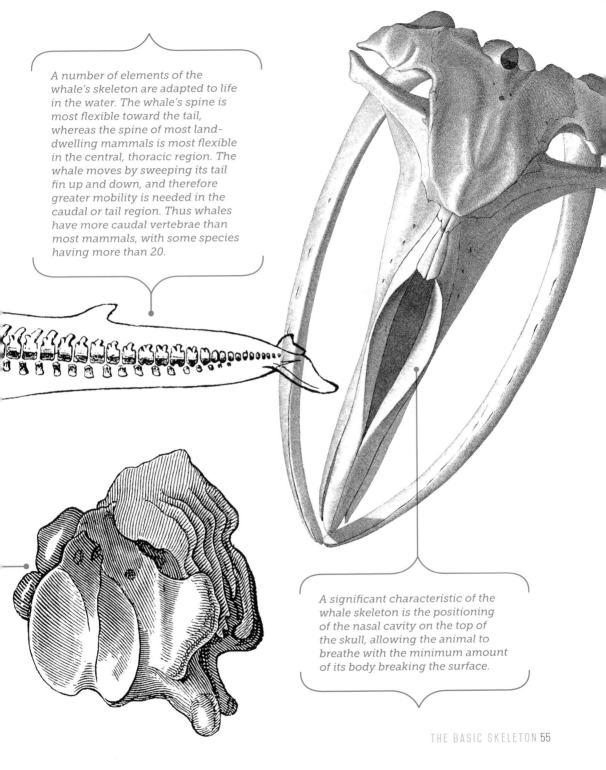

A number of elements of the whale's skeleton are adapted to life in the water. The whale's spine is most flexible toward the tail, whereas the spine of most land-dwelling mammals is most flexible in the central, thoracic region. The whale moves by sweeping its tail fin up and down, and therefore greater mobility is needed in the caudal or tail region. Thus whales have more caudal vertebrae than most mammals, with some species having more than 20.

A significant characteristic of the whale skeleton is the positioning of the nasal cavity on the top of the skull, allowing the animal to breathe with the minimum amount of its body breaking the surface.

FROG

The frog's skeleton is well adapted to getting around by means of enormous leaps—a frog can jump about 20 times its own body length. Its skeleton displays a high level of rigidity to absorb the strains of jumping and the jolt of landing. It has a short spine in which the lower vertebrae are fused, to give a solid base for the thrust of the back legs. The frog has no neck vertebrae, so it cannot move its head. It has also lost its tail, since this would hamper its ability to leap.

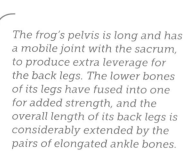

The frog's pelvis is long and has a mobile joint with the sacrum, to produce extra leverage for the back legs. The lower bones of its legs have fused into one for added strength, and the overall length of its back legs is considerably extended by the pairs of elongated ankle bones.

The three sections of its back legs—the femur, the tibia-fibula, and the foot—are of roughly equal length, and at rest they fold into a Z-shape. When the frog jumps the three sections straighten in turn, creating immense leverage and thus a huge leap.

Overall, the frog skeleton has sacrificed flexibility for rigidity. Frogs also lack ribs, so the chest muscles play no part in breathing since there is no rib cage for them to expand and contract. Instead the frog draws air in through its nostrils by lowering the floor of its mouth, then raises the floor of its mouth again to pump air into the lungs.

REPTILES

Reptiles share a number of features that distinguish them from other land animals, such as the inability to regulate their body temperature, a covering of scales rather than hair or feathers, the laying of eggs, and direct development without larval forms.

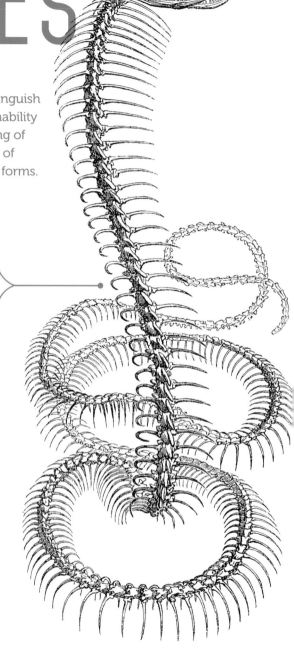

Snakes have no limbs and their movement depends on their belly scales. The snake flexes its spine from side to side and its scales push against irregularities on the surface underneath it, moving the snake forward in a series of lateral motions. Larger snakes use a caterpillar movement, pressing against the ground with a group of belly scales and pushing forward with others to produce a vertically undulating motion.

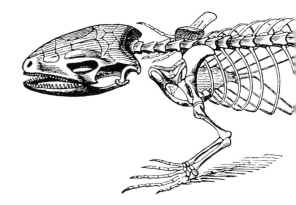

Reptile skeletons have the same general pattern as other animal skeletons, though the head is joined to the spine by a single ball-and-socket joint instead of two, as in mammals, which limits mobility. Most reptiles have a relatively long and thin body shape with legs that stick out sideways. Because this limits how far the limbs can move forward and backward, in comparison with those animals whose legs emerge directly underneath their bodies, many reptiles have a distinctive "swimming" gait, curving the spine from one side to the other so that alternate legs are swung forward. Their body shape facilitates this lateral movement.

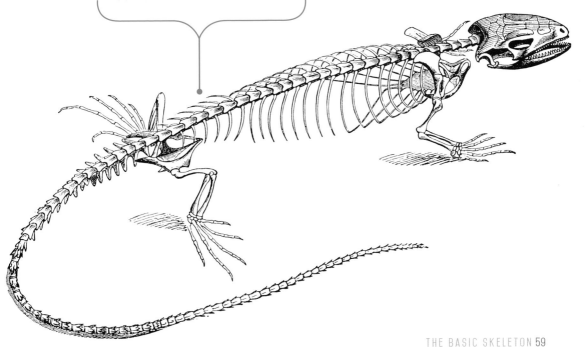

TORTOISE

Tortoises and turtles have both a bony endoskeleton and a hard exoskeleton, the shell. The shell is in two parts, the carapace on top and the plastron below. The flattened ribs and the spine are fused to the shell, so that only the cervical vertebrae and the caudal vertebrae have any mobility. This means that, as in frogs, the rib cage is immobile and thus plays no part in the breathing of these animals. Instead the scapulae expand and contract the lungs to draw in air and expel it. The scapulae articulate to the spine within the rib cage rather than outside it as in all other vertebrates.

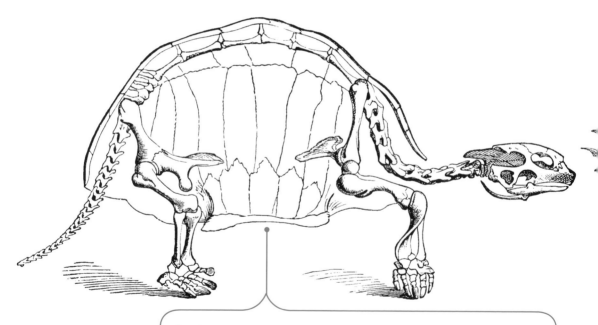

Its rigid structure means that the animal is very well protected from predators. However, as with all exoskeletons the structure is heavy, so the tortoise is unable to move quickly, though turtles do have the advantage of buoyancy in the water, which assists their mobility.

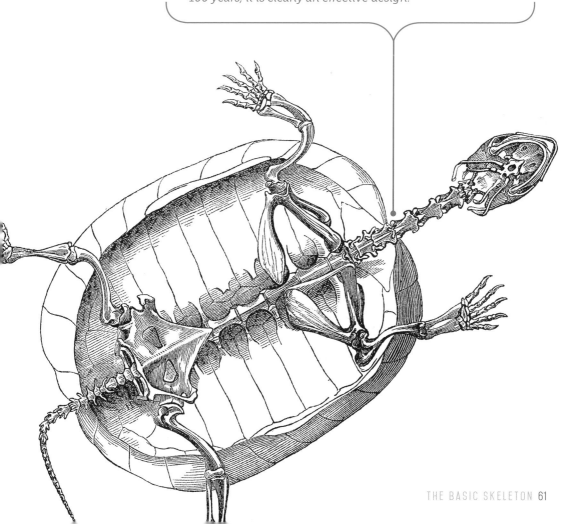

The tortoise's neck is relatively long and flexible, with eight cervical vertebrae rather than the more usual seven. This compensates for the lack of flexibility in its torso, so that it is able to reach for food and can turn to view its surroundings. It also means that the neck and head can retract into the shell for protection, as can the legs, which act to close off the apertures in the shell. Tortoises have relatively large lungs and a low rate of oxygen consumption, so they are able to remain tucked inside their shells for long periods. The design of the tortoise has developed very little since these animals first appeared more than 200 million years ago, and since tortoises have been recorded as living to ages in excess of 100 years, it is clearly an effective design.

DINOSAUR

Complete skeletons of some dinosaurs have been unearthed, so that we have a pretty accurate idea of their structure. And putting questions of scale to one side, it is clear that the architecture of the dinosaur follows the pattern of the other animals we have looked at: a spinal column with a skull at one end and a tail at the other, a rib cage and limbs attached to the frame via pelvic and scapular bones. Triceratops is one of the most recognizable dinosaurs, with its three horns and huge frilled collar. It lived during the latter part of the dinosaur era, about 68 million years ago, and numerous fossil remains have been discovered, the first in Denver in the late 1880s. The skull constituted about one-third of the total skeleton, with its size and robustness making it the most frequently found fossil structure.

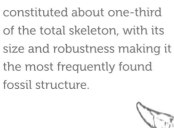

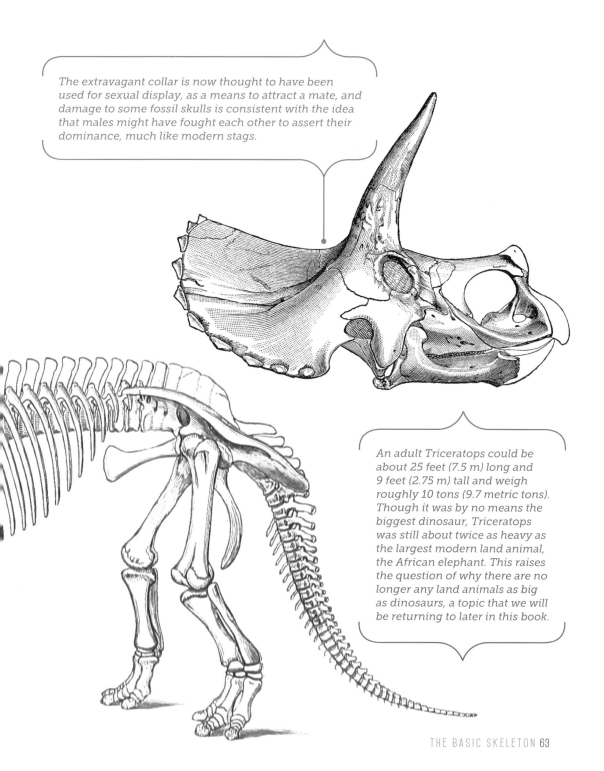

The extravagant collar is now thought to have been used for sexual display, as a means to attract a mate, and damage to some fossil skulls is consistent with the idea that males might have fought each other to assert their dominance, much like modern stags.

An adult Triceratops could be about 25 feet (7.5 m) long and 9 feet (2.75 m) tall and weigh roughly 10 tons (9.7 metric tons). Though it was by no means the biggest dinosaur, Triceratops was still about twice as heavy as the largest modern land animal, the African elephant. This raises the question of why there are no longer any land animals as big as dinosaurs, a topic that we will be returning to later in this book.

DUCK

The skeleton of a bird shows the same basic structure as those of other animals, with a spinal column attached to the head at one end, and appendicular limbs. However, the skeleton has undergone a number of adaptations to enable birds to fly, a feat of which most other vertebrates are incapable. These adaptations are evident from head to tail.

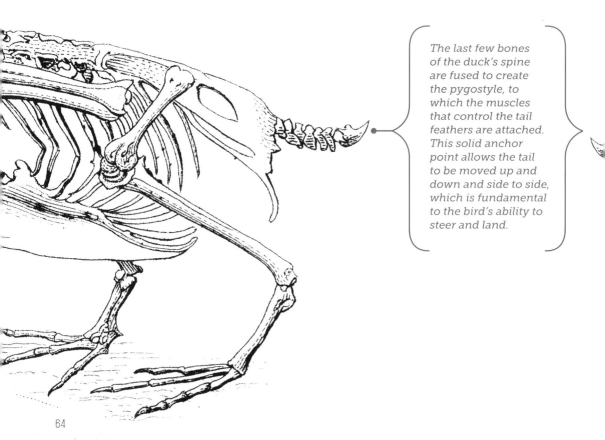

The last few bones of the duck's spine are fused to create the pygostyle, to which the muscles that control the tail feathers are attached. This solid anchor point allows the tail to be moved up and down and side to side, which is fundamental to the bird's ability to steer and land.

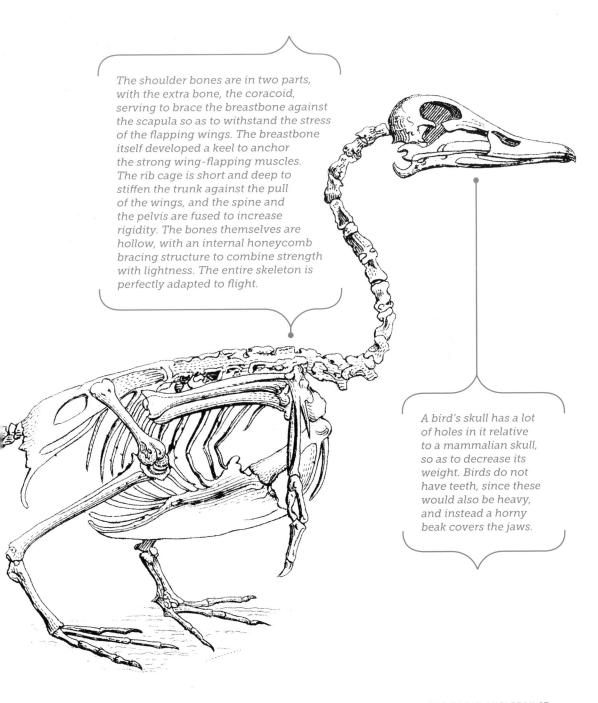

The shoulder bones are in two parts, with the extra bone, the coracoid, serving to brace the breastbone against the scapula so as to withstand the stress of the flapping wings. The breastbone itself developed a keel to anchor the strong wing-flapping muscles. The rib cage is short and deep to stiffen the trunk against the pull of the wings, and the spine and the pelvis are fused to increase rigidity. The bones themselves are hollow, with an internal honeycomb bracing structure to combine strength with lightness. The entire skeleton is perfectly adapted to flight.

A bird's skull has a lot of holes in it relative to a mammalian skull, so as to decrease its weight. Birds do not have teeth, since these would also be heavy, and instead a horny beak covers the jaws.

PENGUIN

The penguin is probably the most unlikely looking of all birds. Most people, asked to visualize a bird, would suggest a rounded body supported on thin legs, a head with a beak supported by a neck, and wings. The bird might have a long neck like a heron, or no neck to speak of like a sparrow, and the relative dimensions of the body parts obviously vary from species to species, but there is a standard bird profile. Even other flightless birds look like birds, however oversized.

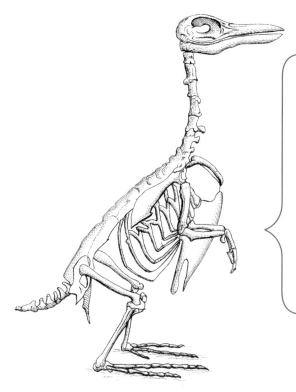

The penguin, with its upright stance and sleek, monochrome plumage seems an entirely different creature altogether. However, the bones of a penguin reveal the tell-tale characteristics of a bird's skeletal structure. The highly developed flange or keel on the breastbone serves in all birds to anchor the wing-flapping muscles, and although the penguin cannot fly, it still has to flap its wings to "fly" through the water. And since water is denser than air, the wing muscles are correspondingly strong and need a solid base. The relative density of water also means that the penguin has no need of lightweight hollow bones, and in fact its solid bones reduce its buoyancy, allowing it to dive.

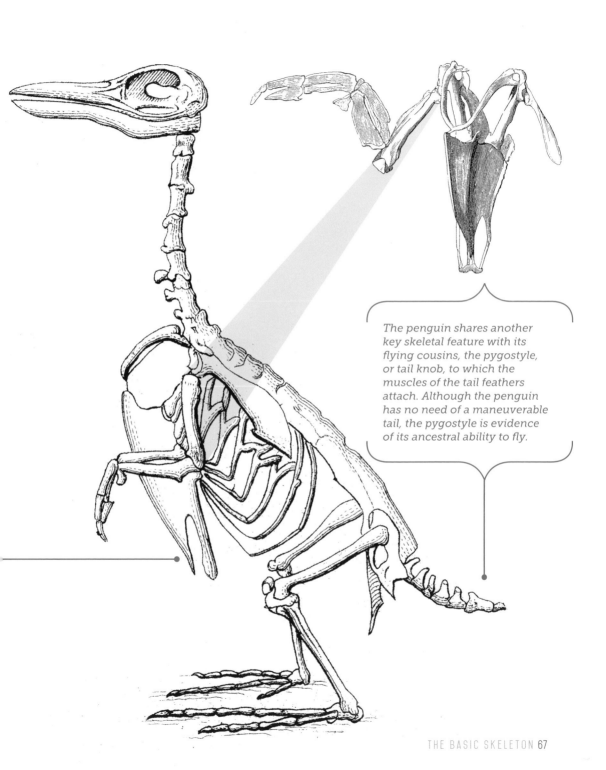

The penguin shares another key skeletal feature with its flying cousins, the pygostyle, or tail knob, to which the muscles of the tail feathers attach. Although the penguin has no need of a maneuverable tail, the pygostyle is evidence of its ancestral ability to fly.

FISH

Fish were the first vertebrates, appearing around 500 million years ago, and they remain the largest class of vertebrates today, with about 30,000 species. The largest bony fish is the ocean sunfish, which can measure up to 11 feet (3.3 m) in length, while the smallest is the dwarf pygmy goby at about ½ inch (1.25 cm) long.

The fish's skull is made up of a number of plates, with a ring of bone to support the eye. The operculum is a plate of bone toward the rear of the fish's head which protects the gills and in some fish forms part of the respiratory system, opening as the mouth closes so that water is forced out over the gills to allow oxygen to be absorbed.

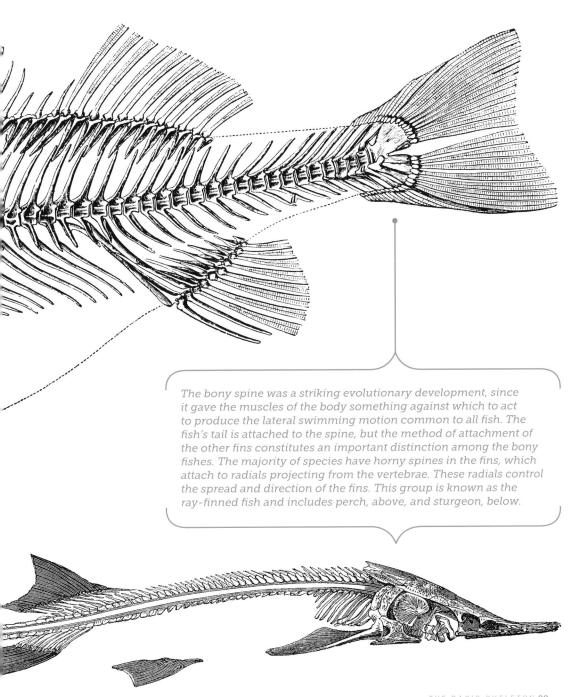

The bony spine was a striking evolutionary development, since it gave the muscles of the body something against which to act to produce the lateral swimming motion common to all fish. The fish's tail is attached to the spine, but the method of attachment of the other fins constitutes an important distinction among the bony fishes. The majority of species have horny spines in the fins, which attach to radials projecting from the vertebrae. These radials control the spread and direction of the fins. This group is known as the ray-finned fish and includes perch, above, and sturgeon, below.

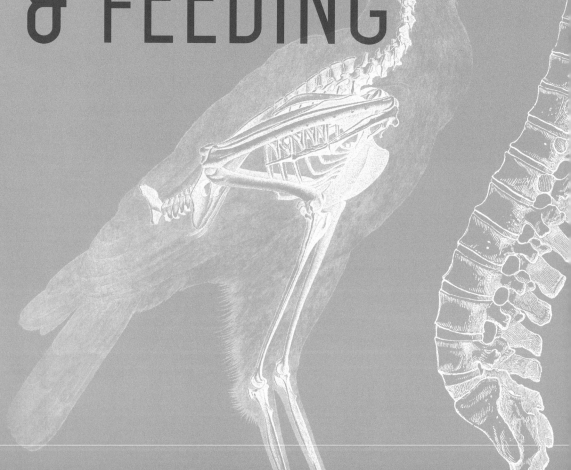

PROTECTION, SUPPORT & FEEDING

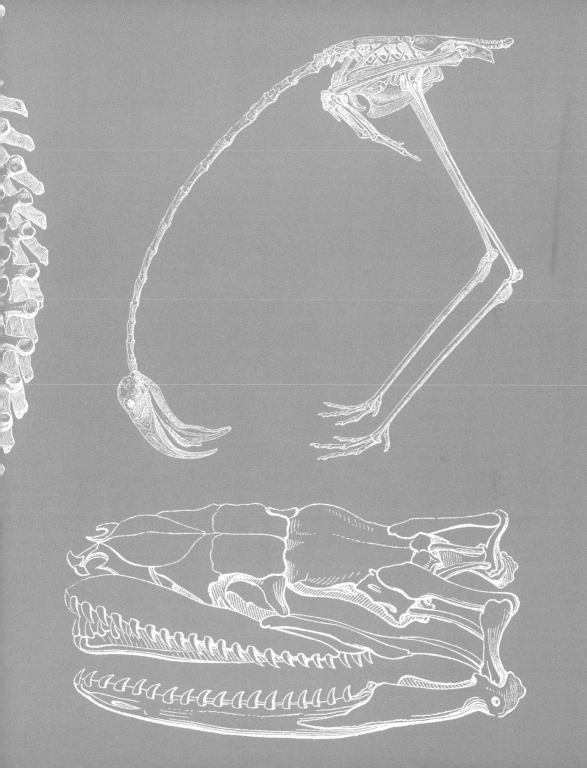

THE HUMAN SKULL

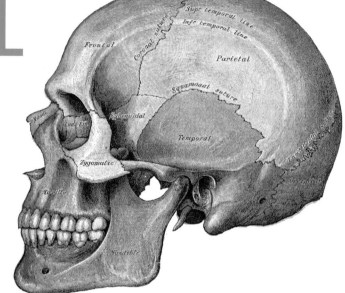

There are nearly 30 separate bones in the human skull, although these are fused together into a solid case by the time an infant reaches the age of one. Many of the bones are paired left and right. The cranium, the main case that holds the brain, is made up of four curved plates, two parietal bones which form the top and the side of the case, the occipital bone which is at the lower back, and the frontal bone which forms the forehead. The parietal bones offer a large surface area for the muscles of the lower jaw to attach to. Paired temporal bones and zygoma or cheekbones make up the lower sides of the brain case, and two more pairs, the maxilla and the mandible bones, form the upper and lower jaws. The sphenoid and ethmoid bones lie at the back of the eye sockets and the nose, and further paired bones form the roof of the mouth and the nasal cavity.

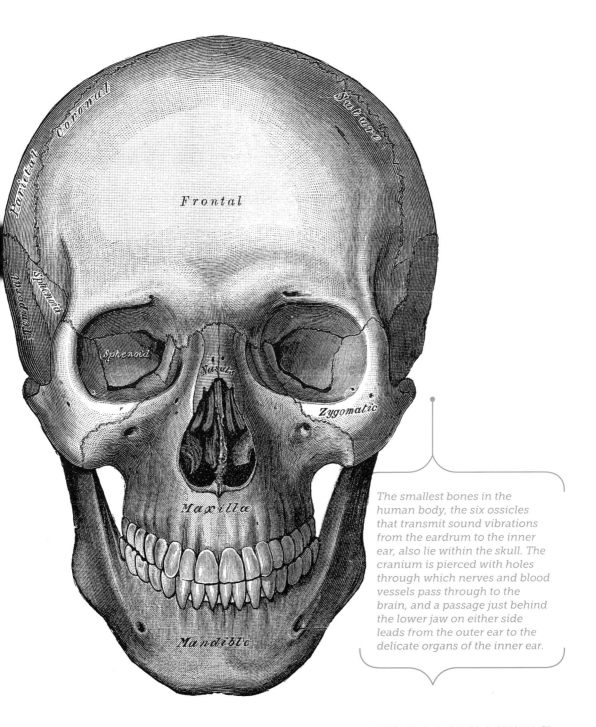

The smallest bones in the human body, the six ossicles that transmit sound vibrations from the eardrum to the inner ear, also lie within the skull. The cranium is pierced with holes through which nerves and blood vessels pass through to the brain, and a passage just behind the lower jaw on either side leads from the outer ear to the delicate organs of the inner ear.

ANIMAL SKULLS

Animal skulls reflect the lifestyles of their owners. The more domed forehead of the human skull relative to other apes, for example, indicates a highly developed cerebral cortex, the part of the brain associated with reasoning and analysis. The shape of the skull is dictated to a large degree by the environment in which an animal lives and the kind of food that it eats.

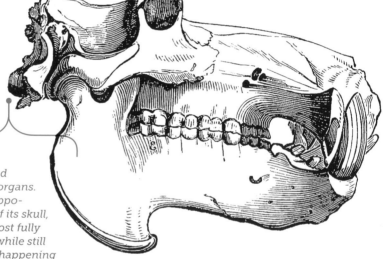

One of the most obvious adaptations is the size and positioning of the sense organs. The eye sockets of the hippopotamus are on the top of its skull, so that it can remain almost fully submerged in the water while still being able to see what is happening around it. The eye sockets of a carnivorous predator such as a tiger are forward-facing to maximize its stereoscopic vision so as to facilitate accurate pursuit of prey, whereas the eye sockets of a herbivorous prey animal are placed more to the side of the skull so as to maximize peripheral vision.

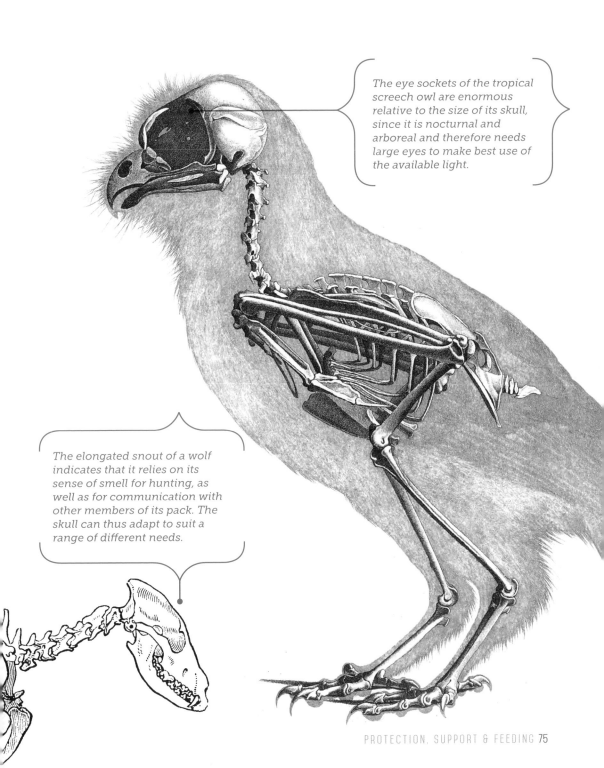

The eye sockets of the tropical screech owl are enormous relative to the size of its skull, since it is nocturnal and arboreal and therefore needs large eyes to make best use of the available light.

The elongated snout of a wolf indicates that it relies on its sense of smell for hunting, as well as for communication with other members of its pack. The skull can thus adapt to suit a range of different needs.

THE HUMAN PELVIS

The word pelvis is derived from the Latin word for "bowl," though in fact the bowl-like shape of the human pelvis is relatively unusual among animal skeletons. Structurally, the pelvis connects the lower limbs to the trunk, and its shape in humans is adapted to the fact that we walk on our "hind" legs. The pelvis is made up of two pairs of three bones: the ilium at the top, the ischium at the lower rear, and the pubis at the front. The bones fuse during puberty to create a rigid framework to support the large muscles that attach the legs to the torso. This bowl also protects the reproductive organs, the bladder, and the lower intestines. There are some notable differences between the male and female pelvis resulting from the fact that women bear children and men do not.

The female pelvis, top, is wider and shallower than the male, and the gap at the bottom is bigger. The male pelvis has a longer sacral promontory, the pointed end of the spine, whereas the female promontory is shorter and does not project so far forward into the pelvic cradle. These variations allow for the largest possible gap through which a baby's head can pass during childbirth. The shape of the female pelvis is a trade-off between the requirements of childbirth and the demands of bipedal locomotion. Too wide a pelvis would make it difficult for a human female to walk efficiently.

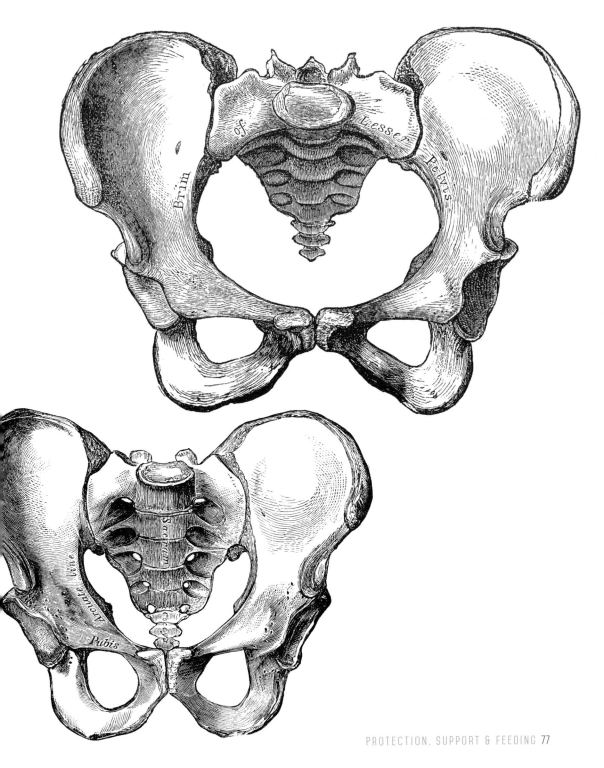

ANIMAL PELVISES

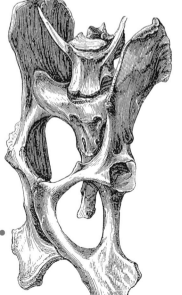

The shape of the pelvis has adapted in different animals according to how they move around.

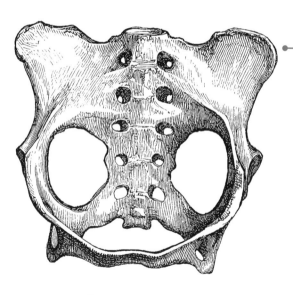

A heavy slow-moving animal, such as a sloth, will have a pelvis with broad flanges of bone to attach the large leg muscles.

A faster, lighter animal, such as a hare, will have a more elongated pelvis for additional leverage.

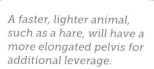

The bones of a bat's pelvic girdle are strongly fused, as are the fibula and tibia, which creates a stable structure that allows the bat to hang upside down when roosting. A bat's legs are rotated 180 degrees relative to most animals, which gives it a characteristic and quite eerie knees-upward profile when it crawls on the ground.

Birds, like humans, have to solve the problem of walking on two legs. The human pelvis has adapted to keep the legs and spine more or less vertical over each other, but most birds do not have a completely upright posture, and they lack heavy tails that would counterbalance their forward leaning, since this would impair their ability to fly. A bird's pelvis is relatively large and is fused to its backbone to create a stable structure for strong muscles that can maintain its thigh bones at a forward-pointing angle. This means that the bird's feet are beneath its center of gravity so that it can keep its balance.

THE HUMAN RIB CAGE

The design of the rib cage is an effective response to the separate functions that this part of the skeleton performs. On the one hand, the ribs have to protect the vital organs in the chest such as the lungs and heart, much as the skull protects the brain. However, unlike the brain, the lungs alter in size during breathing, so a solid case would not work. Instead the casing is made up of a series of separate struts of bone with flexible connections of cartilage to the spine and the sternum or breastbone.

The ribs' flexibility means that they can absorb impacts from the surrounding environment without cracking and damaging the lungs. More importantly, it means that the volume contained within the rib cage can be enlarged and contracted, as the muscles connected to the ribs pull them upward and outward so as to draw air into the lungs before pulling them back in to push the air back out.

The human rib cage has 12 paired ribs. The top seven pairs are connected to the sternum by bands of cartilaginous tissue. The eighth to tenth pairs are connected not to the sternum but to the ribs above them via the same kind of cartilaginous bands. The final two ribs do not come round to connect to the rest of the rib cage at the front, shown right, but simply project from the spine.

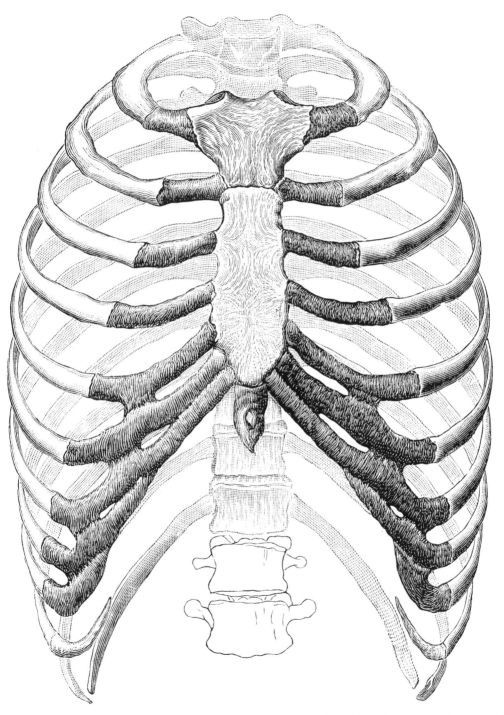

THE WHALE RIB CAGE

The rib cage performs the same functions in other mammals as it does in humans, so the general structure of a flexible cage is much the same. However, there are variations that demonstrate evolutionary adaptation to particular aspects of an animal's lifestyle or environment.

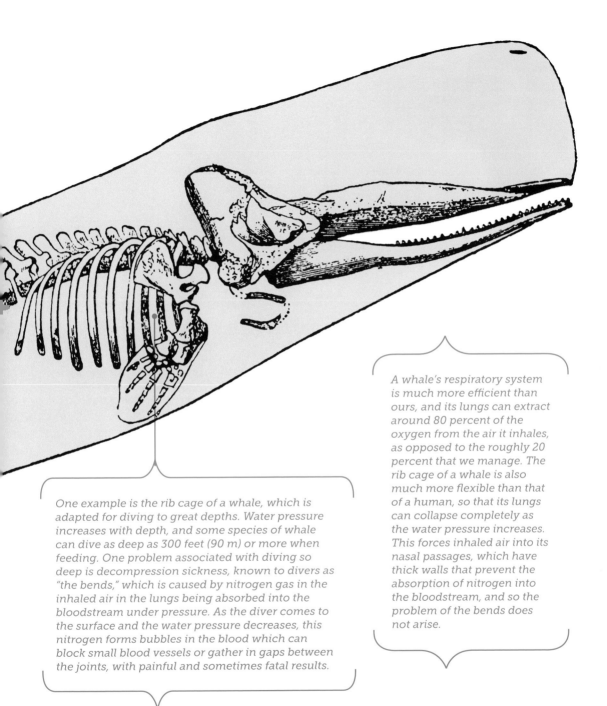

One example is the rib cage of a whale, which is adapted for diving to great depths. Water pressure increases with depth, and some species of whale can dive as deep as 300 feet (90 m) or more when feeding. One problem associated with diving so deep is decompression sickness, known to divers as "the bends," which is caused by nitrogen gas in the inhaled air in the lungs being absorbed into the bloodstream under pressure. As the diver comes to the surface and the water pressure decreases, this nitrogen forms bubbles in the blood which can block small blood vessels or gather in gaps between the joints, with painful and sometimes fatal results.

A whale's respiratory system is much more efficient than ours, and its lungs can extract around 80 percent of the oxygen from the air it inhales, as opposed to the roughly 20 percent that we manage. The rib cage of a whale is also much more flexible than that of a human, so that its lungs can collapse completely as the water pressure increases. This forces inhaled air into its nasal passages, which have thick walls that prevent the absorption of nitrogen into the bloodstream, and so the problem of the bends does not arise.

THE HUMAN SPINE

The human spine is made up of 33 bones, and in describing the spine it is conventional to divide these into five groups.

At the top are the seven cervical vertebrae which form the neck. These are relatively shallow plates which anchor the muscles that connect the skull and shoulder blades to keep the skull balanced on the spine.

Below the cervical vertebrae are 12 thoracic vertebrae which connect to the 12 pairs of ribs. These are larger and deeper than the cervical vertebrae since they carry more of the weight of the body, and the next five, the lumbar vertebrae, are larger still. These anchor the big muscles that twist the lower back and bear a lot of strain. The condition known as a "slipped disc," when the cartilage joints between the vertebrae bulge out and press on the nerves that connect with the spinal cord, is most common in this region.

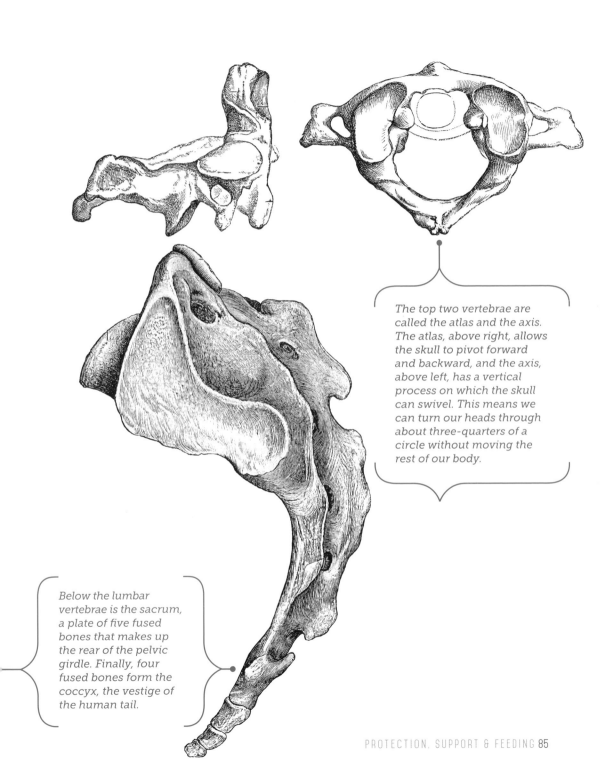

The top two vertebrae are called the atlas and the axis. The atlas, above right, allows the skull to pivot forward and backward, and the axis, above left, has a vertical process on which the skull can swivel. This means we can turn our heads through about three-quarters of a circle without moving the rest of our body.

Below the lumbar vertebrae is the sacrum, a plate of five fused bones that makes up the rear of the pelvic girdle. Finally, four fused bones form the coccyx, the vestige of the human tail.

ANIMAL SPINES

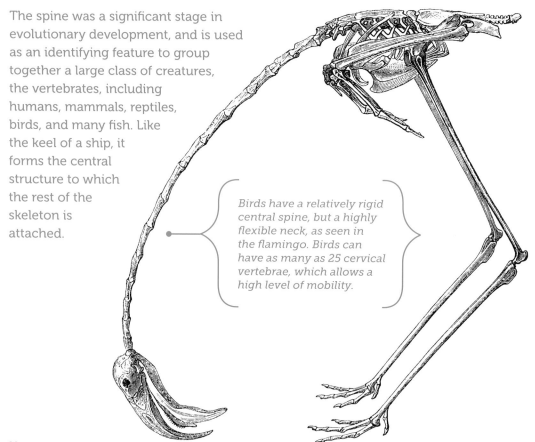

The spine was a significant stage in evolutionary development, and is used as an identifying feature to group together a large class of creatures, the vertebrates, including humans, mammals, reptiles, birds, and many fish. Like the keel of a ship, it forms the central structure to which the rest of the skeleton is attached.

Birds have a relatively rigid central spine, but a highly flexible neck, as seen in the flamingo. Birds can have as many as 25 cervical vertebrae, which allows a high level of mobility.

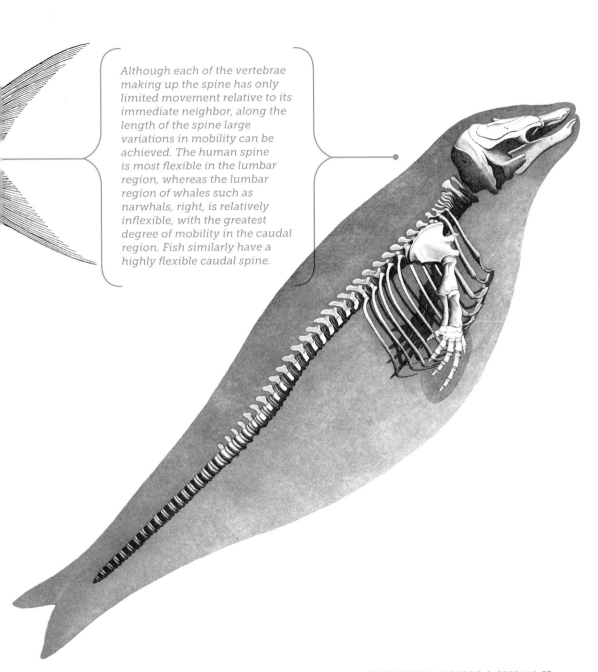

Although each of the vertebrae making up the spine has only limited movement relative to its immediate neighbor, along the length of the spine large variations in mobility can be achieved. The human spine is most flexible in the lumbar region, whereas the lumbar region of whales such as narwhals, right, is relatively inflexible, with the greatest degree of mobility in the caudal region. Fish similarly have a highly flexible caudal spine.

THE HUMAN
JAW

Two sets of paired bones make up the human jaw. The upper pair, the maxillae, form the top of the mouth, the underside of the eye socket, and the floor and side walls of the nose.

The lower jaw, the mandible, consists of two tightly fused curved bones that create a horseshoe shape. The joint of the lower jaw with the cranium is relatively mobile, so that as well as moving up and down to bite, the lower jaw can move forward and backward and from side to side to some extent to facilitate chewing. The main muscle of the lower jaw, the temporalis muscle, is anchored to the flat part of the side of the cranium, while the masseter muscles which move the jaw forward and backward attach to the cheekbones.

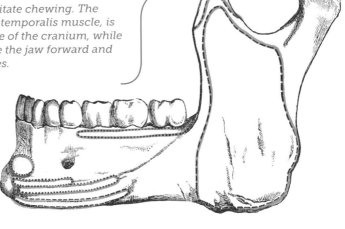

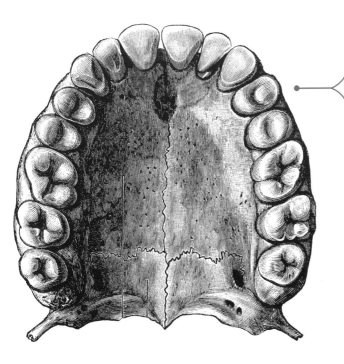

An adult human has 32 teeth, comprising incisors and canines for cutting and tearing, and molars and premolars for grinding. This variety reflects the fact that humans are omnivorous and do not have a specialized diet. The part of the jaw in which the teeth are anchored is made up of spongy bone with cavities in it for the roots of the teeth. If the teeth are lost—because of old age, for instance—this part of the jaw will wear down, giving the appearance that the lower part of the mouth has collapsed inward.

ANIMAL JAWS

Animal skulls and jaws are adapted in different ways depending on what the animal eats. The main difference is between carnivores, the meat-eaters, and herbivores, the plant-eaters.

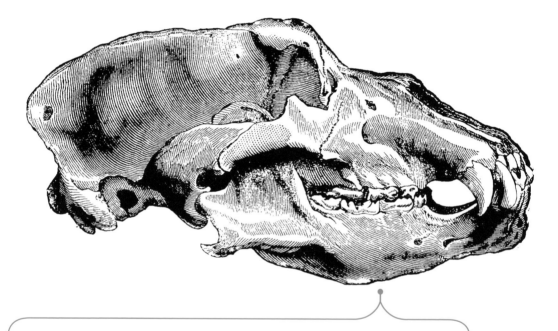

Carnivores tend to have rounded skulls with short, heavy jaws. The robust skull gives a solid foundation for the muscles of the jaw, and the whole structure is designed to produce a powerful bite. The lower jaw is articulated so as to move up and down rather than laterally, since meat does not require much chewing. For the same reason carnivores do not have many teeth, but those they have are large and sharp, particularly the highly developed canines which are characteristic of all carnivores, from bats and cats to tigers and bears.

Conversely, animals that eat vegetable matter tend to have longer skulls to accommodate more grinding teeth. Since plant material is not so digestible as meat it needs to be chewed thoroughly before being swallowed. Sharp incisors at the front of the jaw shear or cut leaves or grass, and rows of flat, wide molars grind the material to a pulp.

The jaws of herbivores are not so heavy as those of carnivores, but they tend to be well-developed at the back, where the muscles that move the lower jaw from side to side are anchored. This is what gives the skulls of animals like cows, donkeys, rhinos, and antelope a more angular, boxlike shape than those of meat-eaters.

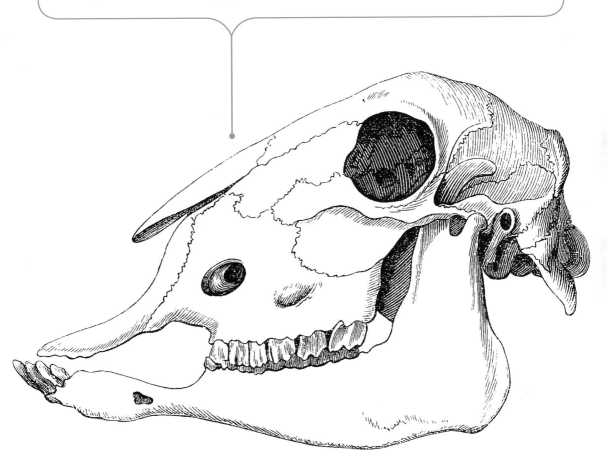

RODENTS

Rodents form an extremely widespread and adaptable group of animals. Amounting to some 40 percent of all animal species, they are found all over the world in every type of environment. There are tree-dwelling species, burrowing species, and semiaquatic species, and some have adapted to the human urban environment. Species range in size from the tiny dormouse, right, to the South American capybara, below.

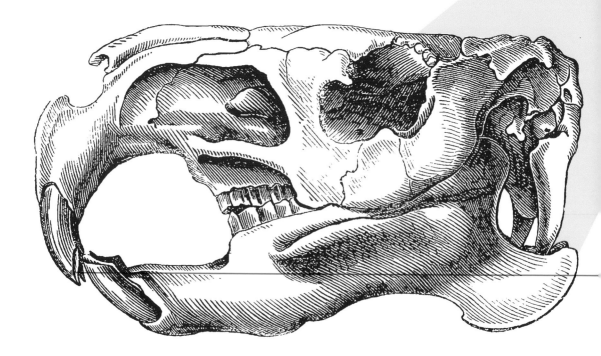

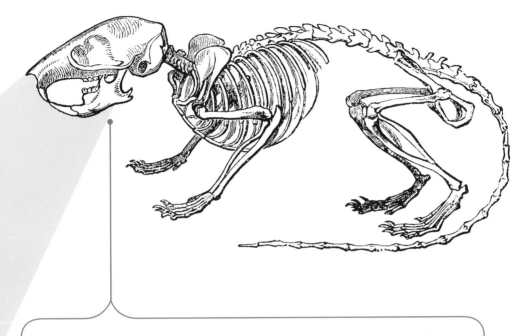

Rodents can chew through tough plant stems and tree bark, and can break open nut shells, even the immensely tough shell of the brazil nut. The large gap between the sharp incisors and the molars allows the rodent to suck in its cheeks or lips to seal off its mouth while it is gnawing, so that indigestible material like nut shells or bark is not swallowed. In comparison with other animals, rodents have large skulls relative to their body size to anchor the strong jaw muscles required for a powerful and efficient bite.

Rodents are distinguished by their extremely large and sharp incisors which are ideal for gnawing and cutting. These teeth are worn down by use and so to compensate they grow continuously throughout the animal's life. They consist of a very hard layer of enamel on the front surface with a softer layer behind, meaning that the teeth are always ground to an extremely sharp edge.

SPECIALIZED JAWS

Animals that eat a variety of food have less specialized jaws and teeth than those that exclusively eat plants or meat. Apes and monkeys, for example, eat fruit, nuts, roots, and berries, but some species such as chimpanzees and baboons, right, will also eat small animals or fish. Their jaws are somewhat elongated, but they have fewer teeth than herbivores and a combination of sharp cutting teeth and flat grinding teeth.

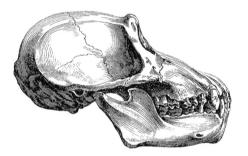

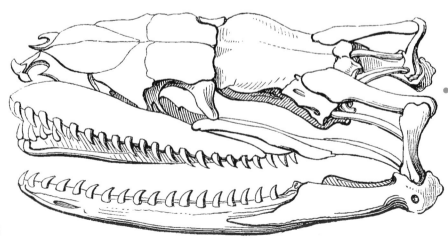

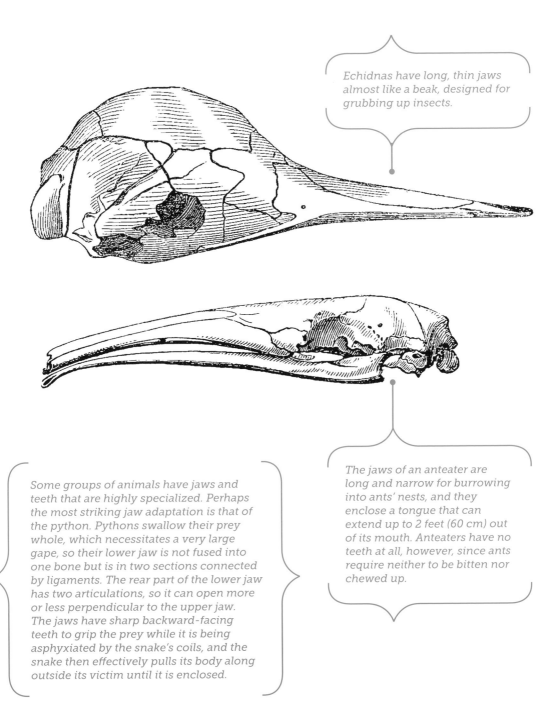

Echidnas have long, thin jaws almost like a beak, designed for grubbing up insects.

The jaws of an anteater are long and narrow for burrowing into ants' nests, and they enclose a tongue that can extend up to 2 feet (60 cm) out of its mouth. Anteaters have no teeth at all, however, since ants require neither to be bitten nor chewed up.

Some groups of animals have jaws and teeth that are highly specialized. Perhaps the most striking jaw adaptation is that of the python. Pythons swallow their prey whole, which necessitates a very large gape, so their lower jaw is not fused into one bone but is in two sections connected by ligaments. The rear part of the lower jaw has two articulations, so it can open more or less perpendicular to the upper jaw. The jaws have sharp backward-facing teeth to grip the prey while it is being asphyxiated by the snake's coils, and the snake then effectively pulls its body along outside its victim until it is enclosed.

WHALE JAWS

The largest jaws in nature belong, not surprisingly, to the
largest animals, the whales, and in particular the toothless or
baleen whales. A whale's skull can take up as much as a third
of its body length, and this greatly elongated skull is mostly
made up of the jaws. Lacking teeth,
baleen whales are unable to bite or
chew large prey. Instead they
have huge mouths so as to
gather sufficient quantities of
the tiny sea creatures that
are their food source.

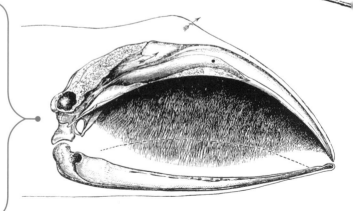

*The upper jaw of a baleen whale
is fused with its skull into a
robust structure that is strong
enough to carry the baleen
plates that hang down to form a
sort of curtain around its mouth.
Baleen is made from keratin, the
same protein that produces
human hair and nails. These
baleen plates act as a sieve,
trapping whatever animals are
present in the water as the whale
forces it out through the plates
with its tongue.*

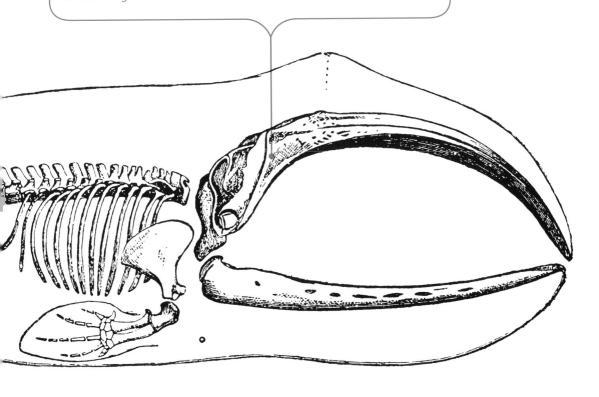

The whale's jaw design varies depending on the feeding habits of the species. Gray whales have relatively short and strong jaws with which they plow up the seabed to dislodge small animals. By contrast, the Greenland or bowhead whale, below, skims the surface of the water with its mouth open all the time, and so its upper jaw forms a huge arch to maximize the volume of water it can take in.

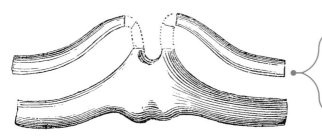

The hyoid arch just beneath the skull anchors the muscles of the tongue, which can weigh as much as 1 ton (900 kg).

BEAKS

The beak was one of the early evolutionary adaptations for flight, since teeth are heavy and would increase the effort required to get the bird off the ground. Instead birds developed a horny sheath that covers the upper and lower jaws and is much lighter. However, even without teeth birds are able to exploit a variety of food sources, from nuts and berries to small mammals and fish, and beaks have evolved in a wide range of shapes and sizes to facilitate the feeding habits of their owners.

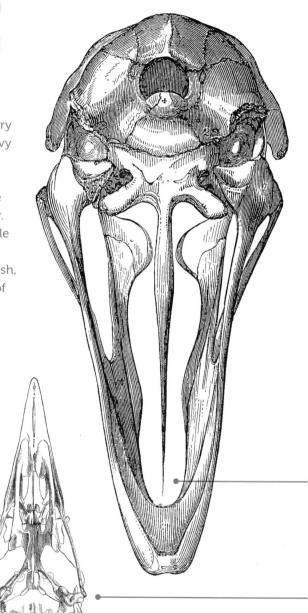

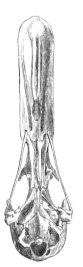

Most birds have nostrils, called nares, located on their beaks, which lead to the nasal cavities in the skull and thence to the respiratory system. In some species, particularly seabirds, these are covered by a horny flap called the operculum, which closes when they dive to keep water out of the nasal passages.

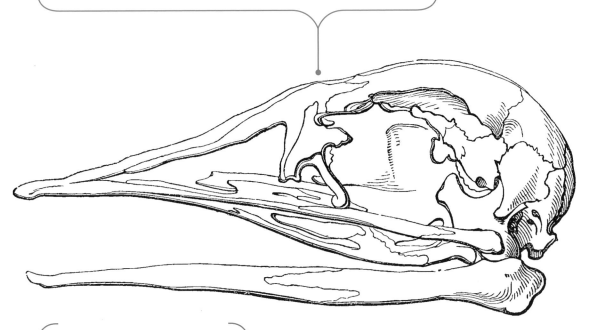

The basic skeletal structure of the jaws of birds is the same across all species. The upper jaw is made up of three bony prongs, one of which attaches to the skull at the forehead while the others attach at either cheek to form a triangular structure.

The lower jaw is made up of two bones that attach at either side of the skull and connect toward the front of the beak, though they extend to differing degrees according to species. The upper and lower jaws are strengthened by an interlacing network of bony struts that allows optimum strength while adding as little weight as possible. The entire structure is then sheathed in a keratinous shell that forms the outer surface of the beak.

BEAKS

Beaks have developed in an extraordinary variety of shapes
and sizes depending on what the beak's owner eats and what
it needs to do to obtain its food.

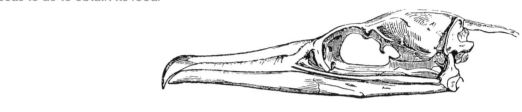

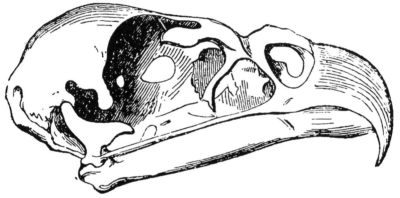

The beak of a raptor such as an eagle has a
characteristic sharp and curved upper jaw
that allows the bird to tear the flesh of its
prey. Carrion feeders such as vultures have a
similar hooked beak shape, as do fish eaters
such as cormorants, above right, though
their beak is longer and more pointed.

Water-fowl such as geese, right,
have broad bills for dabbling in
the water to collect plant matter,
insects, and mollusks. Cranes,
bottom right, have long beaks
with which they probe their
wetland habitat for mollusks,
fish, or vegetable material.

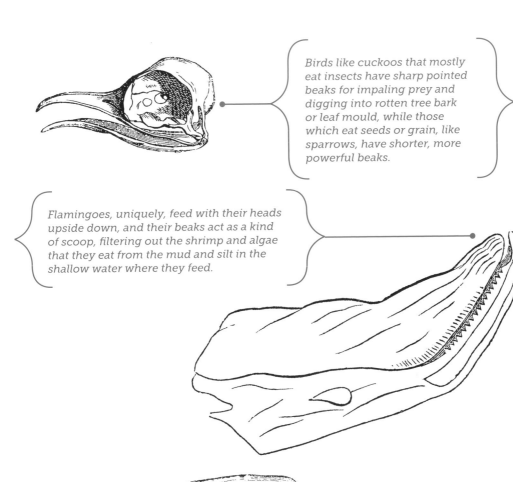

Birds like cuckoos that mostly eat insects have sharp pointed beaks for impaling prey and digging into rotten tree bark or leaf mould, while those which eat seeds or grain, like sparrows, have shorter, more powerful beaks.

Flamingoes, uniquely, feed with their heads upside down, and their beaks act as a kind of scoop, filtering out the shrimp and algae that they eat from the mud and silt in the shallow water where they feed.

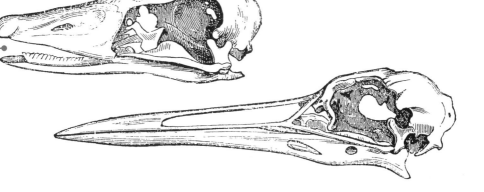

BEAKS

Some birds have highly specialized beaks. Skimmers, below left, are a small family of three species of seabirds that get their name from their practice of skimming low across the surface of the water. Their beaks are long and narrow and, uniquely among bird species, the lower jaw projects beyond the upper jaw. The birds fly low with their beaks open so that the lower jaw cuts into the surface of the water and snatches up any fish near the surface.

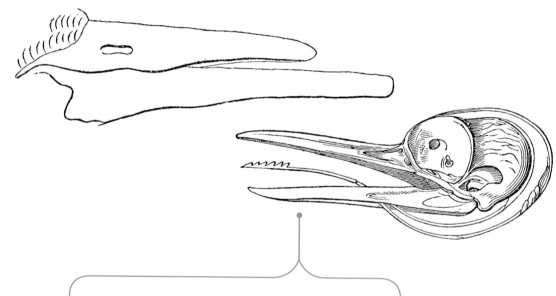

Woodpeckers have a number of skull adaptations that allow them to repeatedly hammer on the trunks of trees to root out the insects that are their main source of food. Their brains are relatively small and snugly padded within the skull so as to minimize the shock from the repeated blows, and there is also shock-absorbent tissue between the beak and the skull. The woodpecker's beak is strong and very sharp, like a chisel, and is kept sharp by the bird's pecking action. The tongue is long and sticky, and has bristles on it to help pull insects out of the tree.

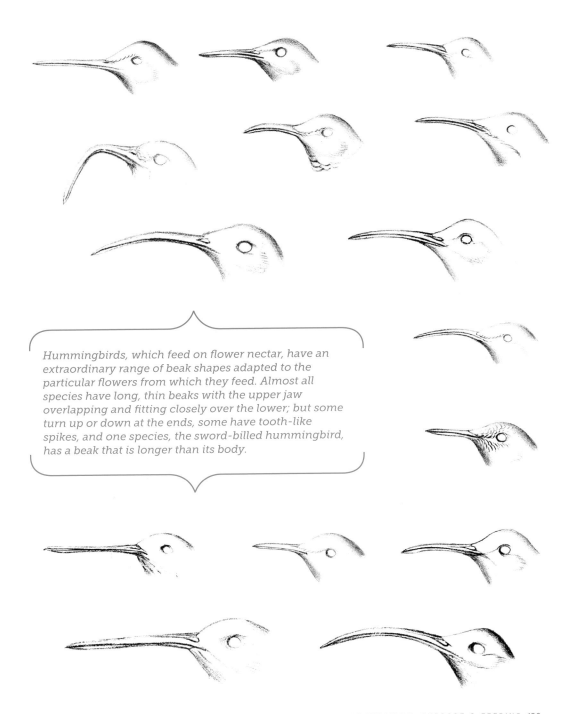

Hummingbirds, which feed on flower nectar, have an extraordinary range of beak shapes adapted to the particular flowers from which they feed. Almost all species have long, thin beaks with the upper jaw overlapping and fitting closely over the lower; but some turn up or down at the ends, some have tooth-like spikes, and one species, the sword-billed hummingbird, has a beak that is longer than its body.

LOCOMOTION

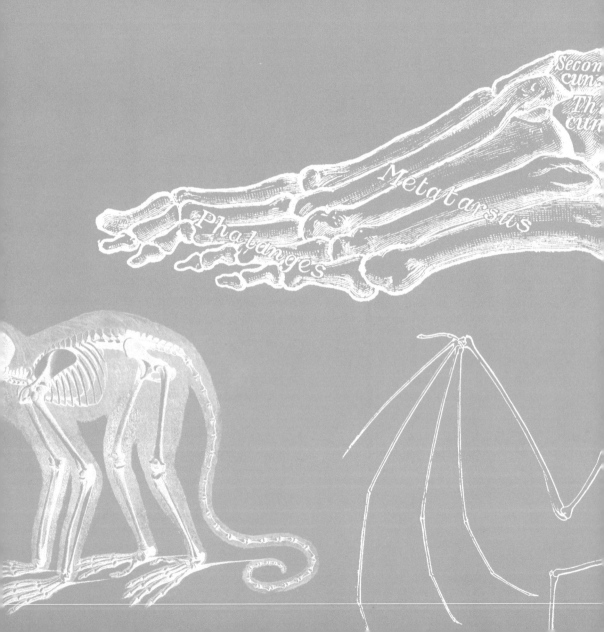

Secon
cun
Th
cun

Metatarsus

Phalanges

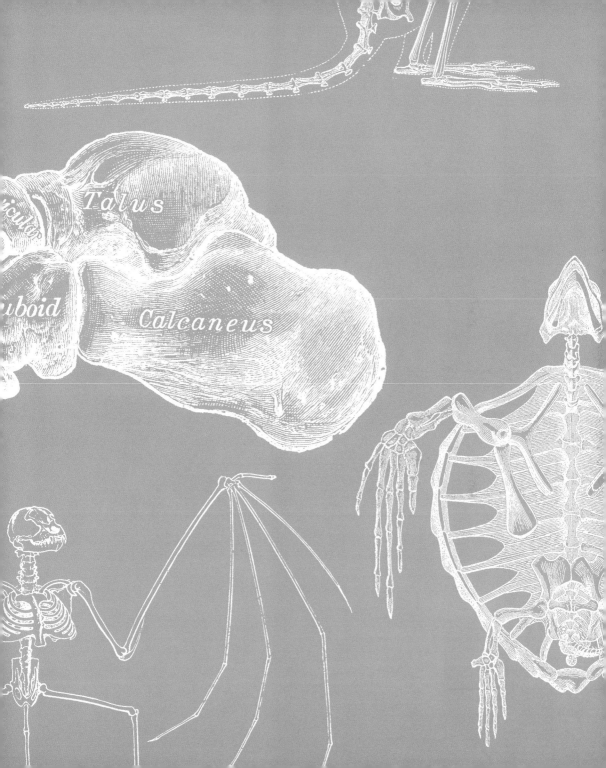

Naviculare

Talus

Cuboid

Calcaneus

LIMBS

The main function of the appendicular limbs is to move their owners around, whether by running, jumping, crawling, flying, or swimming. As we have seen in the case of other bony systems, these different functions can be performed by the same basic set of structures, with variations adapted to specific circumstances.

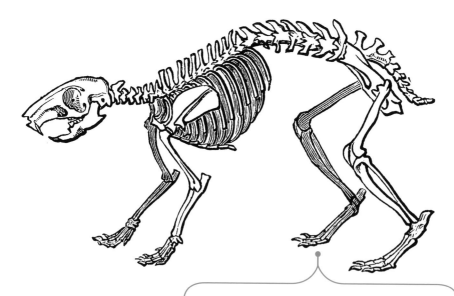

The limbs consist of long columnar bones, a single upper bone connected to the torso and a pair of bones below, with a connecting joint. Below this is a set of relatively short bones arranged in columns that create a platform on which the skeletal structure above is balanced. But this standard pattern has numerous variations.

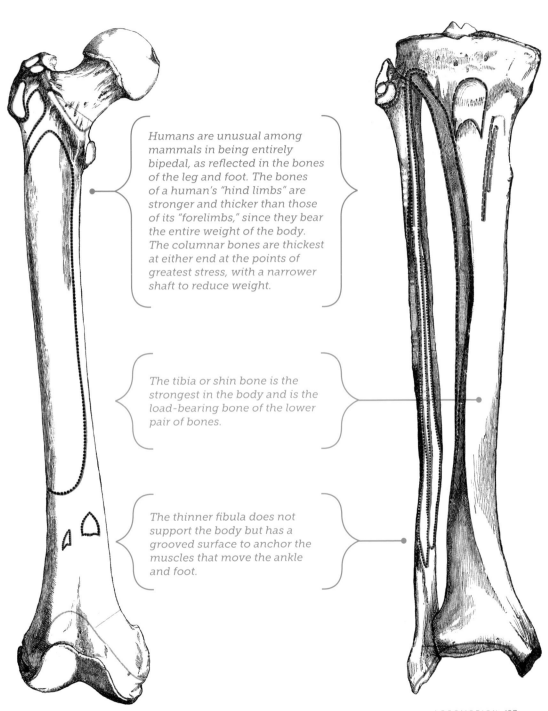

Humans are unusual among mammals in being entirely bipedal, as reflected in the bones of the leg and foot. The bones of a human's "hind limbs" are stronger and thicker than those of its "forelimbs," since they bear the entire weight of the body. The columnar bones are thickest at either end at the points of greatest stress, with a narrower shaft to reduce weight.

The tibia or shin bone is the strongest in the body and is the load-bearing bone of the lower pair of bones.

The thinner fibula does not support the body but has a grooved surface to anchor the muscles that move the ankle and foot.

FEET

There are three basic types of locomotory limb arrangement in mammals, distinguished according to how much of the foot is in contact with the ground. These are plantigrade, where all of the foot is on the ground, as in animals such as bears, humans, and guinea pigs; digitigrade, where the toes are in contact with the ground, as in dogs, cats, and badgers; and unguligrade, where only the tip of the toe touches the ground, as in animals such as cows, sheep, and horses.

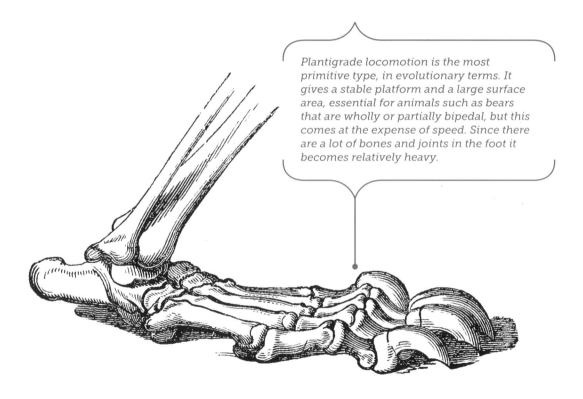

Plantigrade locomotion is the most primitive type, in evolutionary terms. It gives a stable platform and a large surface area, essential for animals such as bears that are wholly or partially bipedal, but this comes at the expense of speed. Since there are a lot of bones and joints in the foot it becomes relatively heavy.

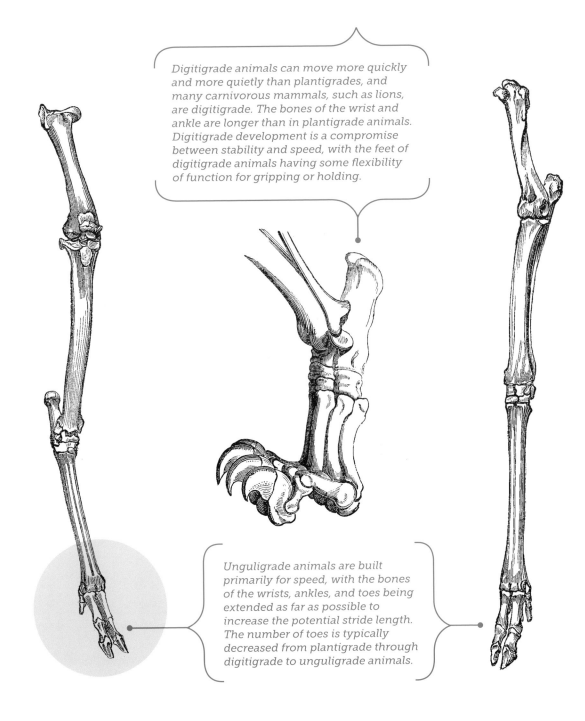

Digitigrade animals can move more quickly and more quietly than plantigrades, and many carnivorous mammals, such as lions, are digitigrade. The bones of the wrist and ankle are longer than in plantigrade animals. Digitigrade development is a compromise between stability and speed, with the feet of digitigrade animals having some flexibility of function for gripping or holding.

Unguligrade animals are built primarily for speed, with the bones of the wrists, ankles, and toes being extended as far as possible to increase the potential stride length. The number of toes is typically decreased from plantigrade through digitigrade to unguligrade animals.

FEET & TOES

The skeletal structure of the foot varies a great deal depending on how the animal moves. The human foot has five toes which are roughly proportionate in length and lie closely aligned with each other to maximize the surface area in contact with the ground. The bones of the foot create a slight arch which flattens out during walking and helps to absorb some of the shock of impact.

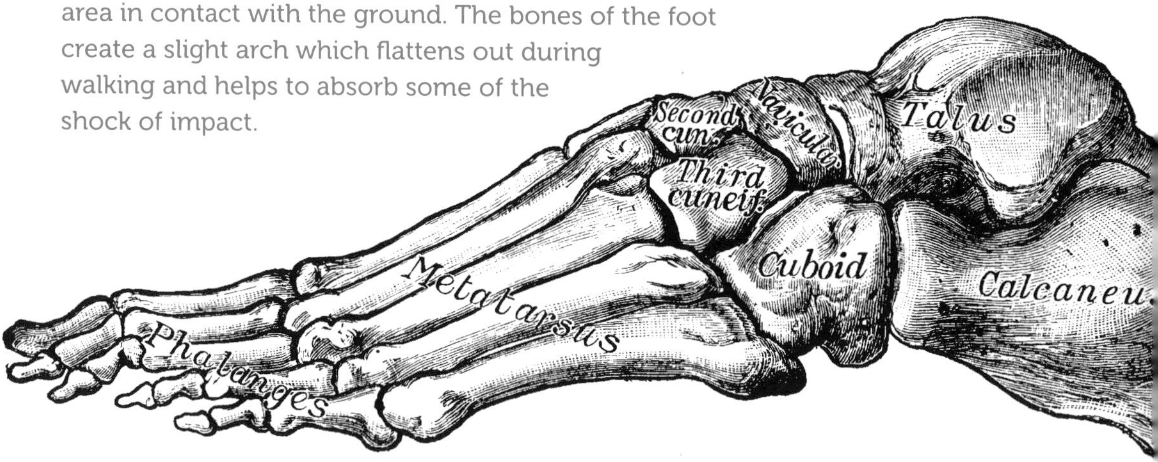

Second cuns.

Navicular

Talus

Third cuneif.

Cuboid

Calcaneu.

Metatarsus

Phalanges

Elephants and hippos are semi-digitigrade, with short, robust toe bones as well as pads of shock-absorbing tissue under their feet.

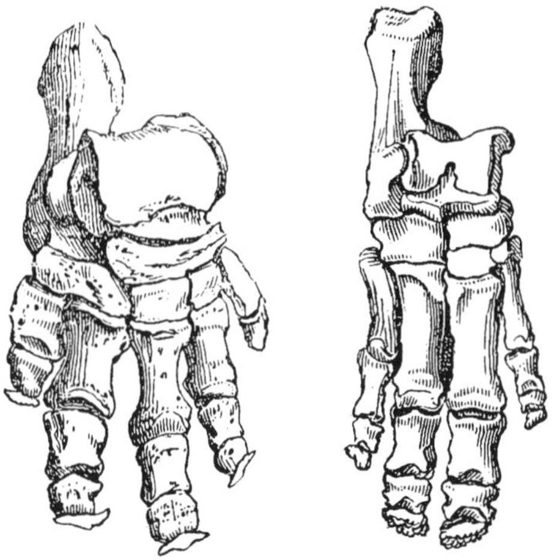

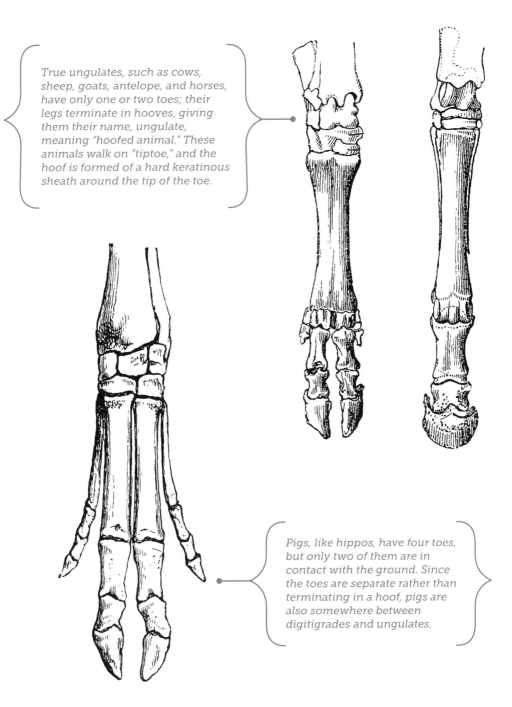

True ungulates, such as cows, sheep, goats, antelope, and horses, have only one or two toes; their legs terminate in hooves, giving them their name, ungulate, meaning "hoofed animal." These animals walk on "tiptoe," and the hoof is formed of a hard keratinous sheath around the tip of the toe.

Pigs, like hippos, have four toes, but only two of them are in contact with the ground. Since the toes are separate rather than terminating in a hoof, pigs are also somewhere between digitigrades and ungulates.

LIMBS FOR RUNNING

The leg bones of a horse exhibit a number of functional differences from the limbs of a human. The shoulder blade is much longer and slimmer, effectively extending the length of the foreleg. The radius and ulna in the foreleg and the tibia and fibula in the hind leg are largely fused to form one bone. This limits any rotational movement and increases the stability of the limb.

In order for humans to be able to rotate the hands, the lower bones of the arms have to be able to move around each other, but this would be of no advantage to a horse, which instead requires maximum stability. The most striking difference from the limbs of a human, however, lies at the distal end.

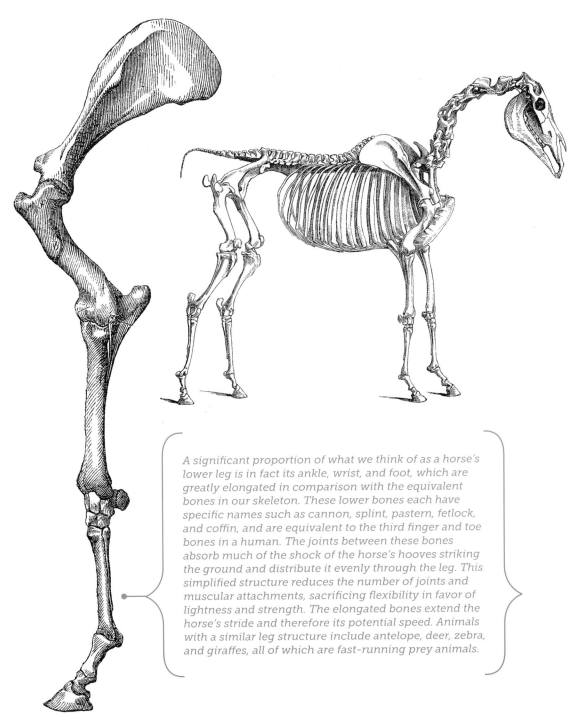

A significant proportion of what we think of as a horse's lower leg is in fact its ankle, wrist, and foot, which are greatly elongated in comparison with the equivalent bones in our skeleton. These lower bones each have specific names such as cannon, splint, pastern, fetlock, and coffin, and are equivalent to the third finger and toe bones in a human. The joints between these bones absorb much of the shock of the horse's hooves striking the ground and distribute it evenly through the leg. This simplified structure reduces the number of joints and muscular attachments, sacrificing flexibility in favor of lightness and strength. The elongated bones extend the horse's stride and therefore its potential speed. Animals with a similar leg structure include antelope, deer, zebra, and giraffes, all of which are fast-running prey animals.

LIMBS FOR JUMPING

Animals that get around by jumping rather than running have a distinctive arrangement of hind limbs. The back legs are longer than the forelegs, as can be seen from the African jumping hare, right, in comparison with the European hare, below, whose front and back legs are nearer the same length since it is a runner rather than a jumper. The ankle and feet bones are also elongated in jumping animals to give maximum leverage.

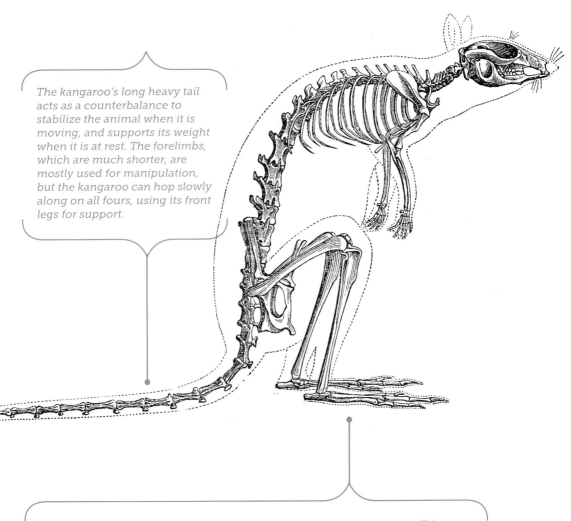

The kangaroo's long heavy tail acts as a counterbalance to stabilize the animal when it is moving, and supports its weight when it is at rest. The forelimbs, which are much shorter, are mostly used for manipulation, but the kangaroo can hop slowly along on all fours, using its front legs for support.

Kangaroos and wallabies belong to the family Macropodidae, meaning "big-footed." The fourth and fifth toes are very long and offer a solid base to push off from. The second and third toes are much shorter and are used for grooming, while the first toe has disappeared altogether. The tibia and fibula are very long and slim relative to the femur, and are partly fused for stability. They form long levers while the femur anchors the powerful thigh muscles that propel the kangaroo at speeds of up to 40 mph (65 km/h).

LIMBS FOR CLIMBING

Climbing animals display various skeletal adaptations for moving around above the ground. The bones are slim and gracile since they are not supporting the animal's bodyweight. The gibbon moves around by swinging from branch to branch, and its forelimbs are disproportionately long compared with its hind limbs, to extend its reach as far as possible. A gibbon can cover as much as 30 feet (9 m) with a single leap. Its finger bones are elongated and slightly recurved to create a hooklike shape that wraps around the tree branches, while the thumb is much shorter. Gibbons do not grip but rather hang from their perches.

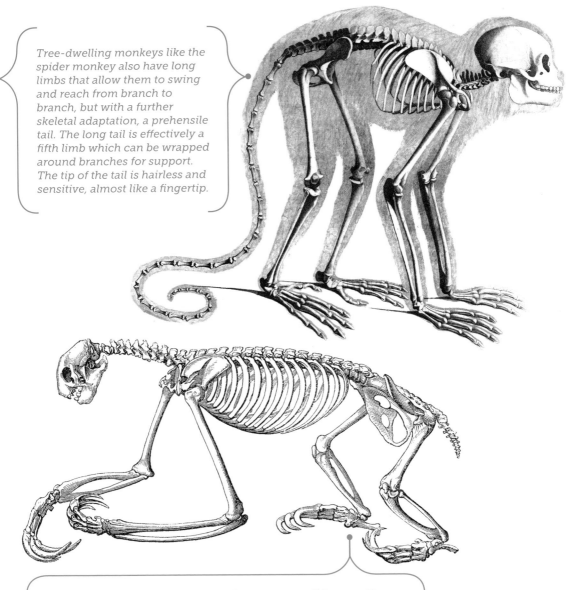

Tree-dwelling monkeys like the spider monkey also have long limbs that allow them to swing and reach from branch to branch, but with a further skeletal adaptation, a prehensile tail. The long tail is effectively a fifth limb which can be wrapped around branches for support. The tip of the tail is hairless and sensitive, almost like a fingertip.

Spider monkeys have the same hand structure as gibbons, with four long fingers and a shorter thumb. This type of structure is most pronounced in the three-toed sloth, which has long fingers and toes finishing in strong curved claws. This mechanism means that sloths can hang upside down from tree branches with very little effort, which allows them to conserve energy.

BIRD LEGS

Birds, like humans, are bipedal —that is, they walk, run, or jump on their hind legs, though unlike humans they walk on their toes. Their skeletons display a number of adaptations to facilitate this, such as the fusion of the pelvis with the spinal column, called the synsacrum, which creates a solid anchorage for the leg muscles. The fibula and tibia are similarly fused to some degree, while the bones of the ankle are fused to the tibia. The lower bones of the foot are also fused to form the tarsometatarsus, the part of the leg immediately above the toes.

These fusions of what in other animals are separate bones reduce the number of joints and therefore the weight, while conserving strength and stability. The bones of most birds also contain air pockets, which reduces weight as well as contributing to respiration, though some diving birds and the large flightless birds have fewer hollow bones.

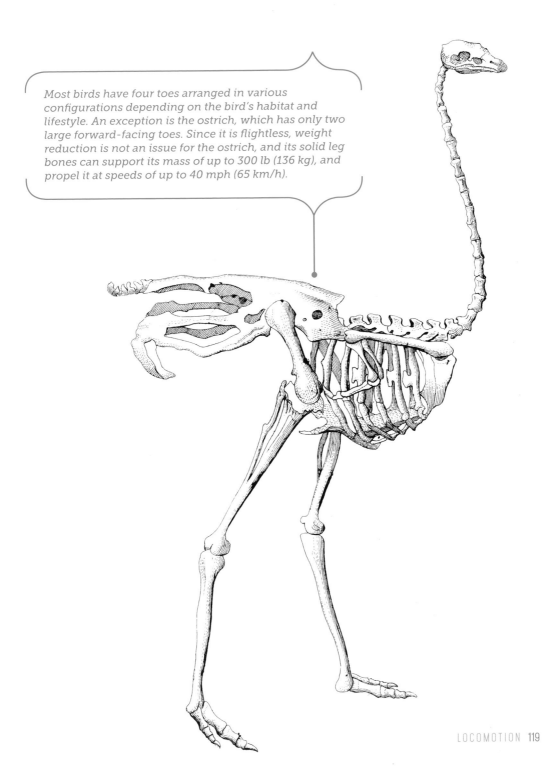

Most birds have four toes arranged in various configurations depending on the bird's habitat and lifestyle. An exception is the ostrich, which has only two large forward-facing toes. Since it is flightless, weight reduction is not an issue for the ostrich, and its solid leg bones can support its mass of up to 300 lb (136 kg), and propel it at speeds of up to 40 mph (65 km/h).

BIRD FEET & TOES

Most birds have three toes pointing forward and one pointing backward, an arrangement known as anisodactyly. Nearly all songbirds and waterbirds have an anisodactylic configuration, which is suitable for perching and, with the addition of webbing between the toes, swimming.

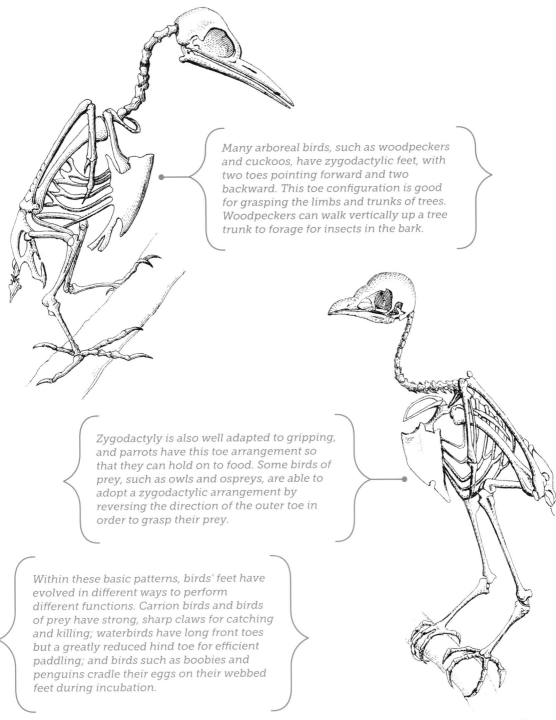

Many arboreal birds, such as woodpeckers and cuckoos, have zygodactylic feet, with two toes pointing forward and two backward. This toe configuration is good for grasping the limbs and trunks of trees. Woodpeckers can walk vertically up a tree trunk to forage for insects in the bark.

Zygodactyly is also well adapted to gripping, and parrots have this toe arrangement so that they can hold on to food. Some birds of prey, such as owls and ospreys, are able to adopt a zygodactylic arrangement by reversing the direction of the outer toe in order to grasp their prey.

Within these basic patterns, birds' feet have evolved in different ways to perform different functions. Carrion birds and birds of prey have strong, sharp claws for catching and killing; waterbirds have long front toes but a greatly reduced hind toe for efficient paddling; and birds such as boobies and penguins cradle their eggs on their webbed feet during incubation.

BAT WINGS

Bats are the only animals apart from birds that can truly fly, since other "flying" animals really only prolong their fall from a height by the use of some kind of parachute of skin. The forelimbs of a bat have developed in such a way that it can take off, land, and maneuver in the air.

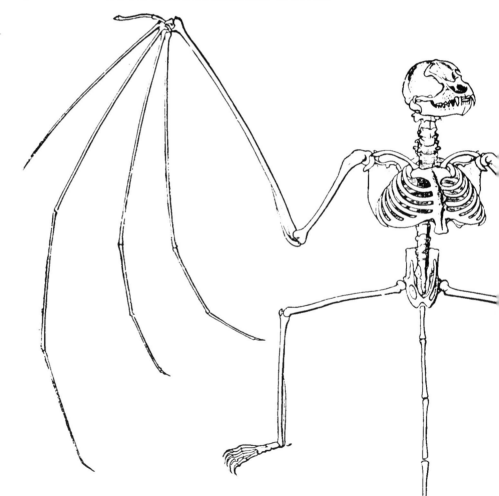

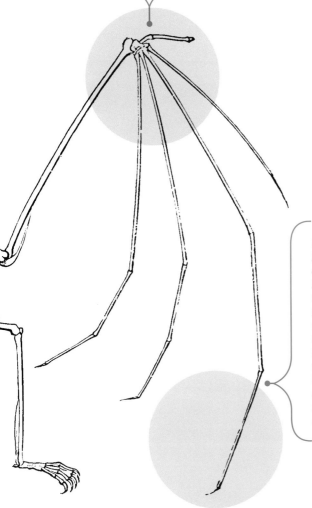

The wings of a bat can be extended or folded with a single muscular action between the humerus and the radius, so that they can be adjusted with the minimum of effort. The wrist joint is highly flexible, so that the wings can be drawn up tightly like an umbrella when the animal is roosting.

With the exception of the thumb, the bones of a bat's forelimbs are increasingly elongated the further they are from the body. The shoulder blades are large so as to anchor the strong wing muscles. The humerus is relatively short compared with the overall length of the forelimb. The ulna is also very short and is often fused with the radius, producing a very strong structure that can support the wings. The finger bones, which support the skin of the wings, are greatly elongated. Effectively, the bat flies by flapping its hands up and down, a mind-boggling achievement.

PTEROSAUR FLIGHT

Like bats, pterosaurs are believed to have flown by means of wings made up of a membrane stretched between its bones. The name for one of the known genuses of pterosaur, the pterodactyl, derives from the Greek words for "winged finger" because, unlike bats, the wing membrane was stretched between the fourth "finger" of the pterosaur and its body.

With only fossils as evidence it is not certain where exactly the membrane attached to the body. Early reconstructions suggested that the wing attached to the femur or the ankle, but there is some evidence that the wing membrane of pterosaurs had stiffening fibers, somewhat like bird feathers, which would mean that the wing could retain its aerodynamic shape without having to be held taut by the lower limb.

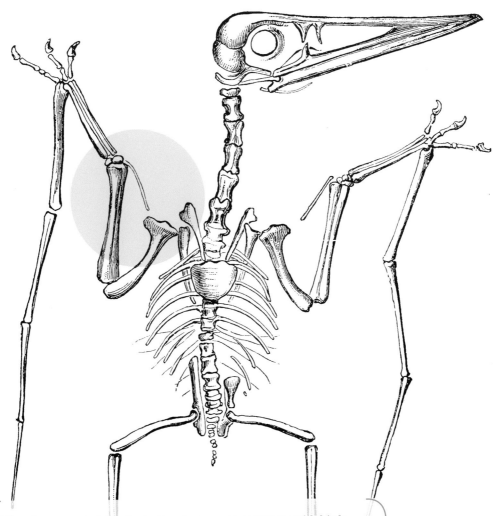

The pterosaur skeleton had other features in common with birds. The thoracic vertebrae were partly fused to create a stable base for the shoulder blades, and pterosaurs had a keeled breastbone for the attachment of the powerful flight muscles. Also, as in birds, the bones of pterosaurs were hollow and contained air sacs, which act as extensions of the lungs and increase the supply of oxygen. An enhanced oxygen supply is important for the high-energy work of flying. This also suggests that pterosaurs might have been warm-blooded, generating energy for flapping flight through burning calories, rather than cold-blooded, like reptiles, as reptiles would find it difficult to produce enough energy to flap their wings for long periods and would only be able to soar.

THE WINGS
OF BIRDS

The forelimbs of birds have the same pattern as other animals: humerus, radius and ulna, and carpal bones. These form the leading edge of the bird's wing, while its surface area is made up of feathers, which are composed of keratin, the same material that makes up human fingernails and hair and animal horns and hooves.

The bird's "thumb," known as the alula, flight feathers attached to it. During flight these feathers lie flush with the leading edge of the wing, but they are extended when the bird is flying slowly or landing, much like the slats on the leading edge of an airplane wing, so as to prevent the bird from stalling.

The overall shape of the wing varies depending on how the bird flies. Soaring seabirds such as albatrosses have long, thin wings, and the albatross also has locking joints in its forelimbs to reduce strain during extended soaring flight. Conversely, birds such as hummingbirds, living in confined areas such as forests, where greater maneuverability is needed, have short, wide wings.

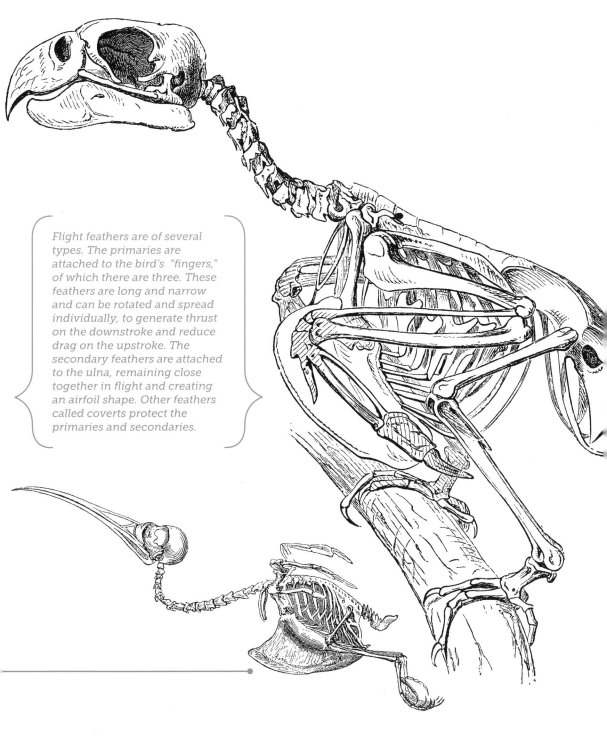

Flight feathers are of several types. The primaries are attached to the bird's "fingers," of which there are three. These feathers are long and narrow and can be rotated and spread individually, to generate thrust on the downstroke and reduce drag on the upstroke. The secondary feathers are attached to the ulna, remaining close together in flight and creating an airfoil shape. Other feathers called coverts protect the primaries and secondaries.

FINS &
PADDLES

Terrestrial mammals rely on their limbs for locomotion, primarily the rear limbs which supply most of the motive power. Many marine mammals lack hind limbs altogether or have only vestigial limbs, and so the main source of power for locomotion is the spine or, in animals like the sea lion and the walrus, the forelimbs.

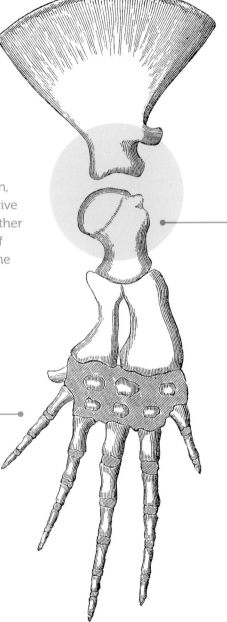

The phalanges or finger bones can be as long as the arm bones, and are widely spaced to maximize the area of the flipper. Whale species have more phalanges than other mammals, as many as 14, to increase the potential flipper area.

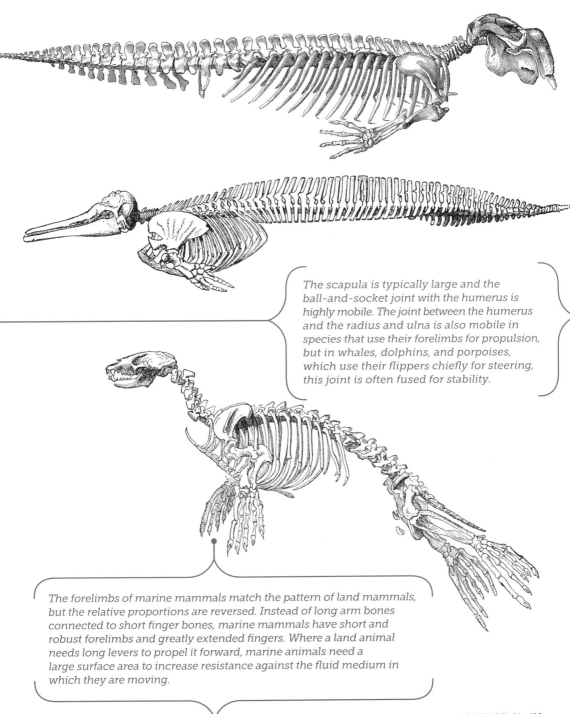

The scapula is typically large and the ball-and-socket joint with the humerus is highly mobile. The joint between the humerus and the radius and ulna is also mobile in species that use their forelimbs for propulsion, but in whales, dolphins, and porpoises, which use their flippers chiefly for steering, this joint is often fused for stability.

The forelimbs of marine mammals match the pattern of land mammals, but the relative proportions are reversed. Instead of long arm bones connected to short finger bones, marine mammals have short and robust forelimbs and greatly extended fingers. Where a land animal needs long levers to propel it forward, marine animals need a large surface area to increase resistance against the fluid medium in which they are moving.

TURTLE LIMBS

Sea turtles display very clearly the types of skeletal adaptations that characterize animals that use their forelimbs for locomotion. Turtles and tortoises are unique in having their pectoral girdles inside their rib cages. The turtle's pectoral girdle is made up of the arch-shaped scapula and the coracoid, the same structural elements as are found in birds, which of course also use their forelimbs for locomotion. The coracoid flares out toward the end into a plate, and the bones together form a three-pronged structure that offers a wide area for the attachment of the main muscles of the front flippers.

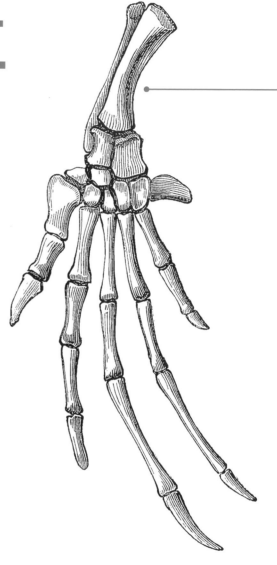

The humerus is short and flattened, with projections at the head and part way along the shaft for muscle attachment. The radius and ulna are also short and flattened, and in some species the bones are fused. The joint with the wrist is mostly cartilaginous, which means that the entire arm structure is stiff and resistant to rotation. The most obvious adaptation for forelimb propulsion can be seen in the wrist and hands. The wrist bones are flat and wide, and the phalanges or finger bones are enormously elongated to create a large flipper area. The digits are longer than the bones of the arm, and are almost a third of the length of the entire animal.

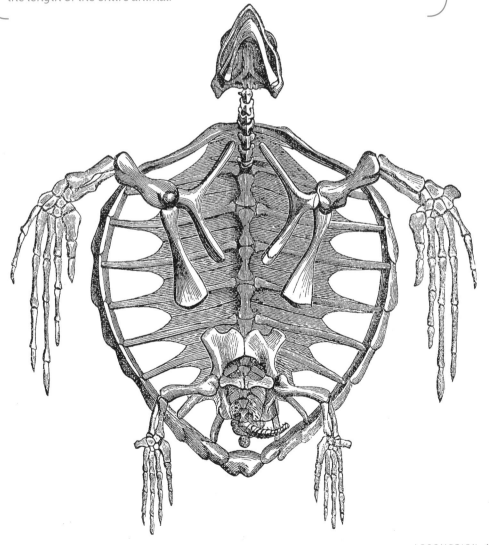

MANIPULATION

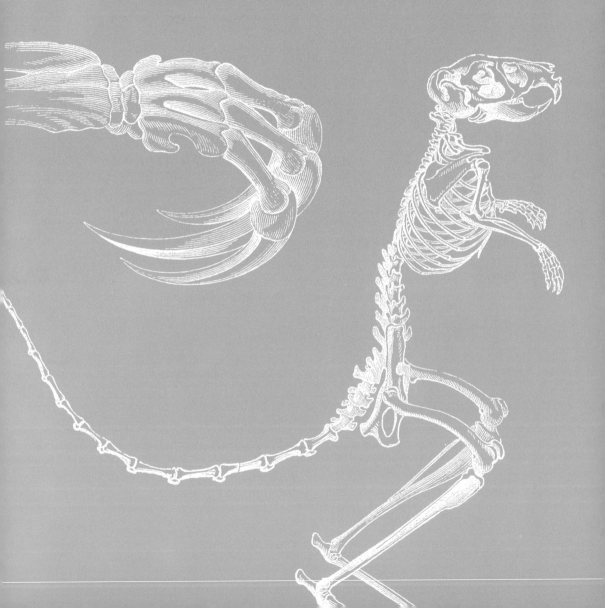

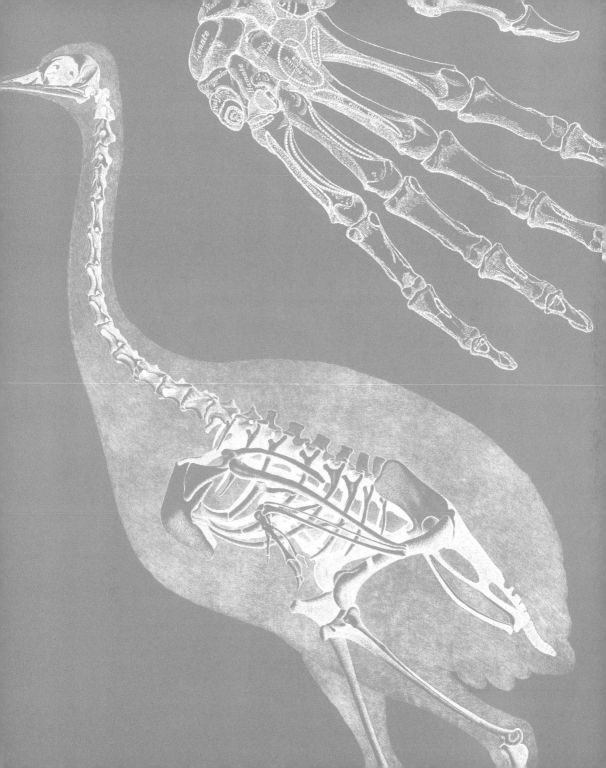

FORELIMBS

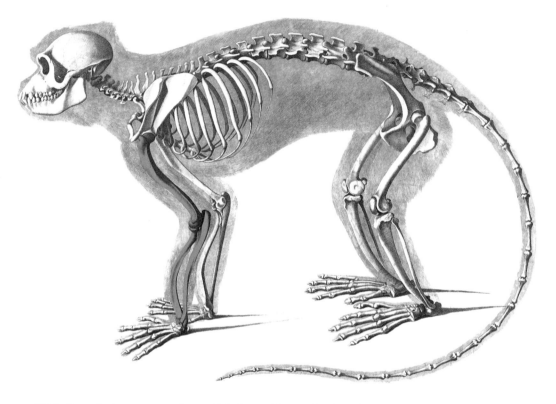

With the obvious exception of birds and bats, the hind limbs of most animals are used chiefly for moving them around. The forelimbs often perform this function as well, but in many animals they are also adapted for other purposes. This means that forelimbs typically display more functional adaptations than hind limbs, with the standard structure—of a single bone at the top connected to two lower bones and then to wrist and finger bones—being developed in different patterns and proportions.

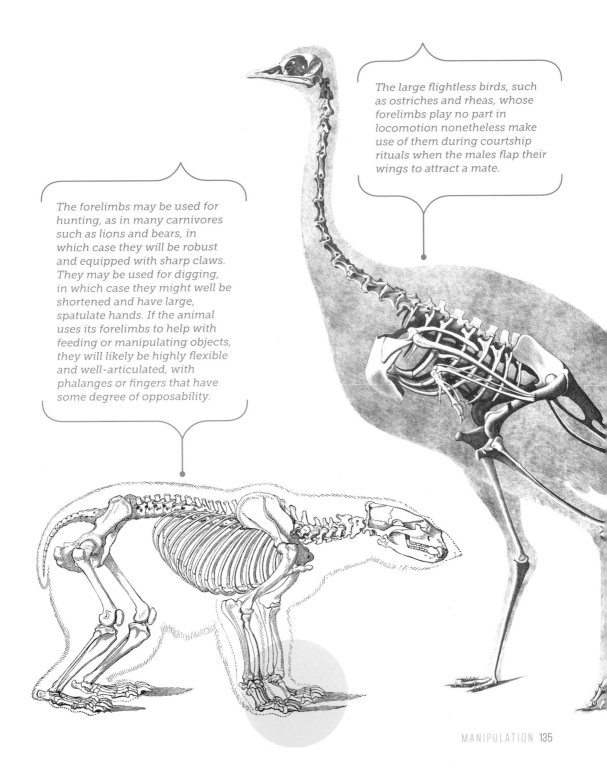

The large flightless birds, such as ostriches and rheas, whose forelimbs play no part in locomotion nonetheless make use of them during courtship rituals when the males flap their wings to attract a mate.

The forelimbs may be used for hunting, as in many carnivores such as lions and bears, in which case they will be robust and equipped with sharp claws. They may be used for digging, in which case they might well be shortened and have large, spatulate hands. If the animal uses its forelimbs to help with feeding or manipulating objects, they will likely be highly flexible and well-articulated, with phalanges or fingers that have some degree of opposability.

FORELIMBS

Digging animals such as anteaters, opposite below, and armadillos show how the structure of the forelimb can be adapted for a specific purpose. Armadillos are a family of South American animals consisting of about 20 different species, all of which dig to make burrows to live in as well as to root up ants, worms, larvae, and other small animals for food.

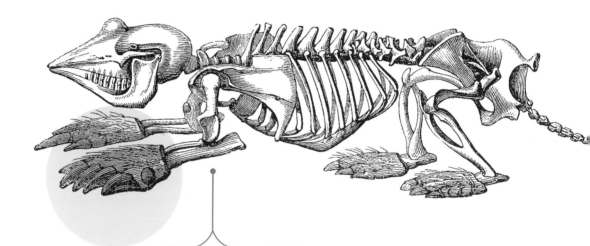

Armadillo skeletons are all adapted for digging, some of them spectacularly so. The pink fairy armadillo is a nocturnal species about 6 inches (15 cm) long that lives in the scrubby grasslands of central Argentina. Its squat forelimbs are large relative to its overall size, with a broad scapula and short, wide arm bones, and the armadillo has immense claws on both front and back feet. Indeed, its claws are so big as to make it difficult for the animal to walk on a hard surface, but they are ideally suited to digging into the compact sandy soil that constitutes its usual environment.

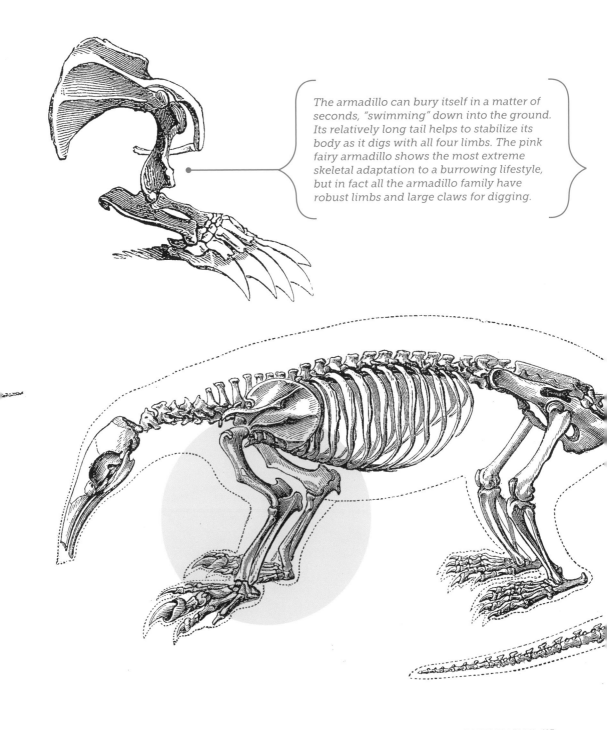

The armadillo can bury itself in a matter of seconds, "swimming" down into the ground. Its relatively long tail helps to stabilize its body as it digs with all four limbs. The pink fairy armadillo shows the most extreme skeletal adaptation to a burrowing lifestyle, but in fact all the armadillo family have robust limbs and large claws for digging.

FORELIMBS

Some animals show a marked disproportion between front and rear limbs, related to some aspect of their lifestyle.

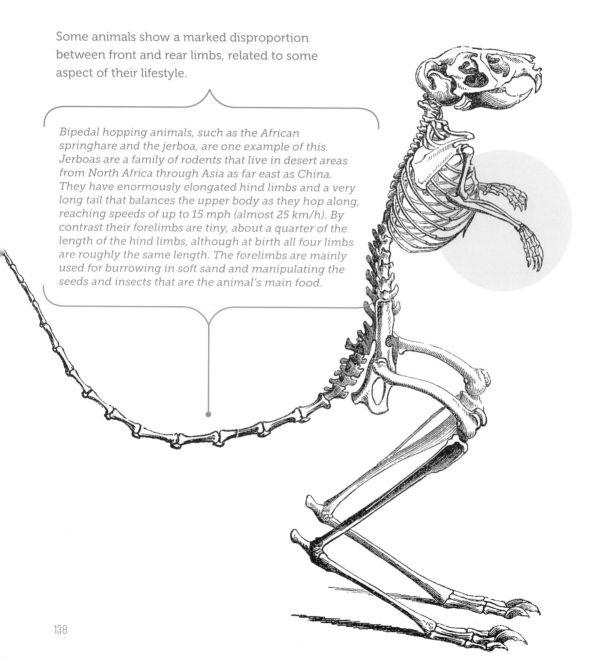

Bipedal hopping animals, such as the African springhare and the jerboa, are one example of this. Jerboas are a family of rodents that live in desert areas from North Africa through Asia as far east as China. They have enormously elongated hind limbs and a very long tail that balances the upper body as they hop along, reaching speeds of up to 15 mph (almost 25 km/h). By contrast their forelimbs are tiny, about a quarter of the length of the hind limbs, although at birth all four limbs are roughly the same length. The forelimbs are mainly used for burrowing in soft sand and manipulating the seeds and insects that are the animal's main food.

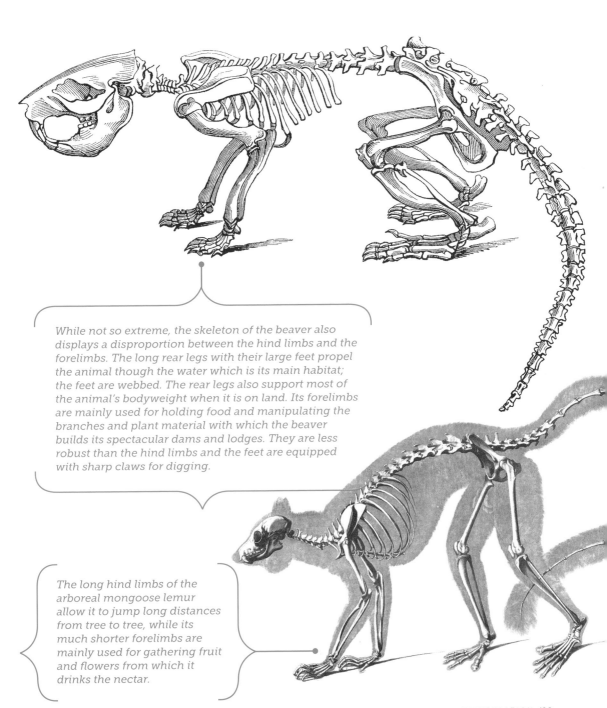

While not so extreme, the skeleton of the beaver also displays a disproportion between the hind limbs and the forelimbs. The long rear legs with their large feet propel the animal though the water which is its main habitat; the feet are webbed. The rear legs also support most of the animal's bodyweight when it is on land. Its forelimbs are mainly used for holding food and manipulating the branches and plant material with which the beaver builds its spectacular dams and lodges. They are less robust than the hind limbs and the feet are equipped with sharp claws for digging.

The long hind limbs of the arboreal mongoose lemur allow it to jump long distances from tree to tree, while its much shorter forelimbs are mainly used for gathering fruit and flowers from which it drinks the nectar.

HUMAN HAND

The animal "hand" is based on a five-digit structure with variations depending on the animal's lifestyle and habitat, the most versatile of which belongs to our species. The human hand, in combination with the human brain, is what has given us such a huge evolutionary advantage over other animals, the key to its usefulness being the opposable thumb.

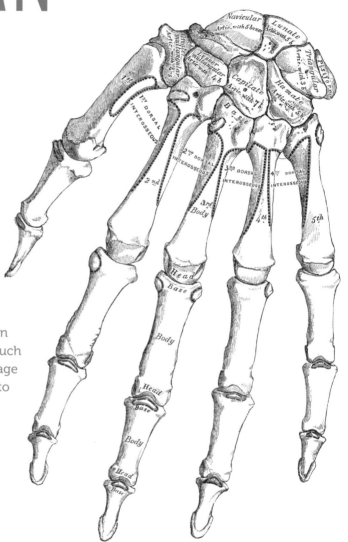

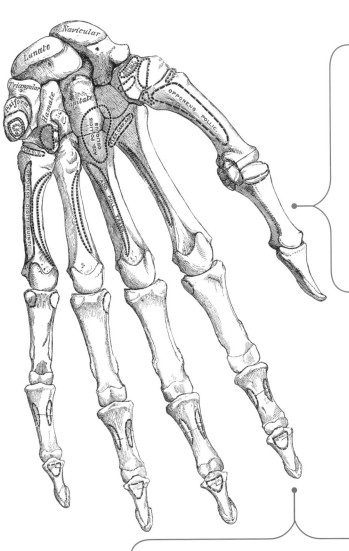

Many animals have opposable thumbs, but that of humans is particularly well developed. The thumb is relatively long in comparison with the other fingers, and the joint at the base of the thumb where this connects to the bones of the hand is highly mobile, allowing the thumb to move in two planes. These two features mean that the thumb can precisely touch the index fingertip to create a pincer—in fact, humans can touch each fingertip with our thumb.

This precision allows a huge amount of manipulative control, so that we can pick up tiny objects, perform delicate operations, and make accurate movements at close range. The design of our hand also means that we can grip objects of various shapes, from flat plates to cylinders to spheres. In combination with the flexible wrist and lower arm bones, this versatility gives us an enormous range of functional options, from threading a needle to throwing a ball, from typing an essay to steering a go-kart, from opening an envelope to cutting down a tree.

OPPOSABLE THUMBS

A comparison of the hands of various primates indicates clearly how much more highly adapted the human hand is to precise manipulation. At rest the human thumb, below left, extends to about half the length of the other fingers, and the bones of the fingers and the thumb are roughly the same size and articulate to the same degree. The thumb can also project to a wide angle relative to the fingers.

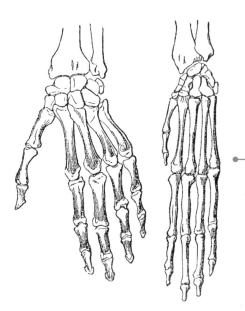

The hand of the chimpanzee is similar to a human's in terms of relative finger length, but its thumb is more in line with the other fingers and therefore less mobile. The orangutan's thumb is only about a third of the length of the other fingers, and so the precise fingertip-to-thumb pincer movement is not available to this animal. However, its long fingers can bend round further than human fingers, meaning that they can grip effectively by coiling inward against the palm.

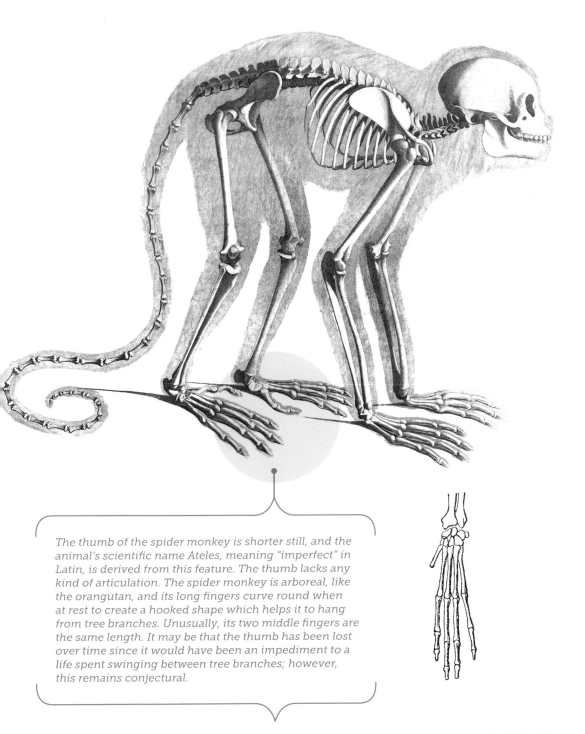

The thumb of the spider monkey is shorter still, and the animal's scientific name Ateles, meaning "imperfect" in Latin, is derived from this feature. The thumb lacks any kind of articulation. The spider monkey is arboreal, like the orangutan, and its long fingers curve round when at rest to create a hooked shape which helps it to hang from tree branches. Unusually, its two middle fingers are the same length. It may be that the thumb has been lost over time since it would have been an impediment to a life spent swinging between tree branches; however, this remains conjectural.

HANDS & CLAWS

As is true of most of the rest of the skeleton, the "hands" of an animal may become adapted over time to fulfill a specific function.

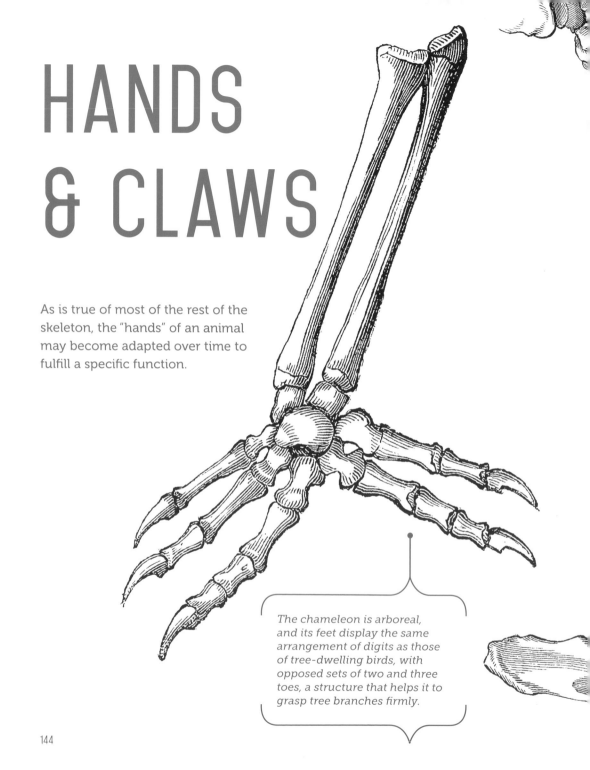

The chameleon is arboreal, and its feet display the same arrangement of digits as those of tree-dwelling birds, with opposed sets of two and three toes, a structure that helps it to grasp tree branches firmly.

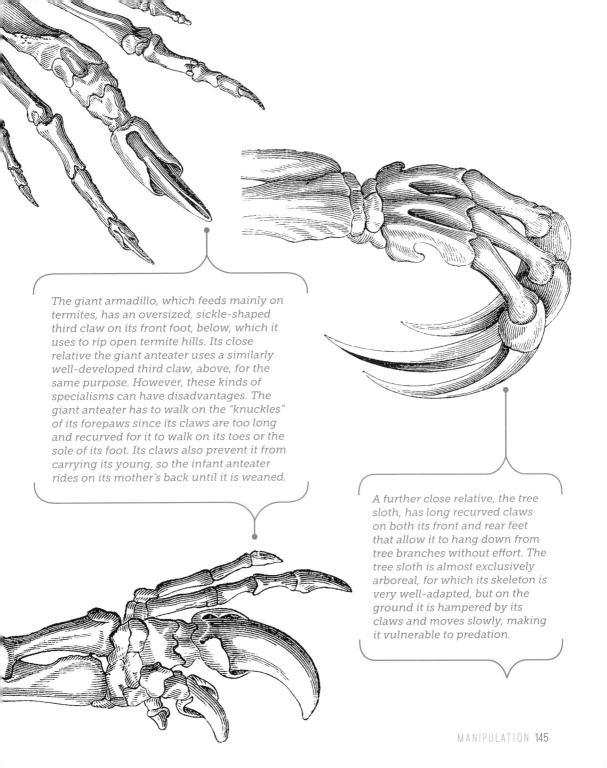

The giant armadillo, which feeds mainly on termites, has an oversized, sickle-shaped third claw on its front foot, below, which it uses to rip open termite hills. Its close relative the giant anteater uses a similarly well-developed third claw, above, for the same purpose. However, these kinds of specialisms can have disadvantages. The giant anteater has to walk on the "knuckles" of its forepaws since its claws are too long and recurved for it to walk on its toes or the sole of its foot. Its claws also prevent it from carrying its young, so the infant anteater rides on its mother's back until it is weaned.

A further close relative, the tree sloth, has long recurved claws on both its front and rear feet that allow it to hang down from tree branches without effort. The tree sloth is almost exclusively arboreal, for which its skeleton is very well-adapted, but on the ground it is hampered by its claws and moves slowly, making it vulnerable to predation.

EVOLUTION OF STRUCTURES

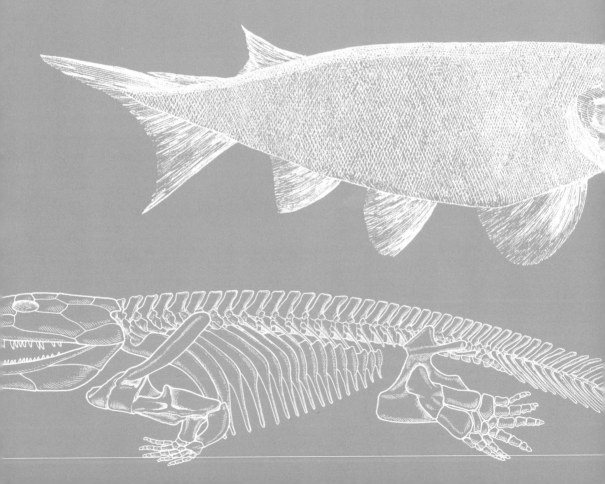

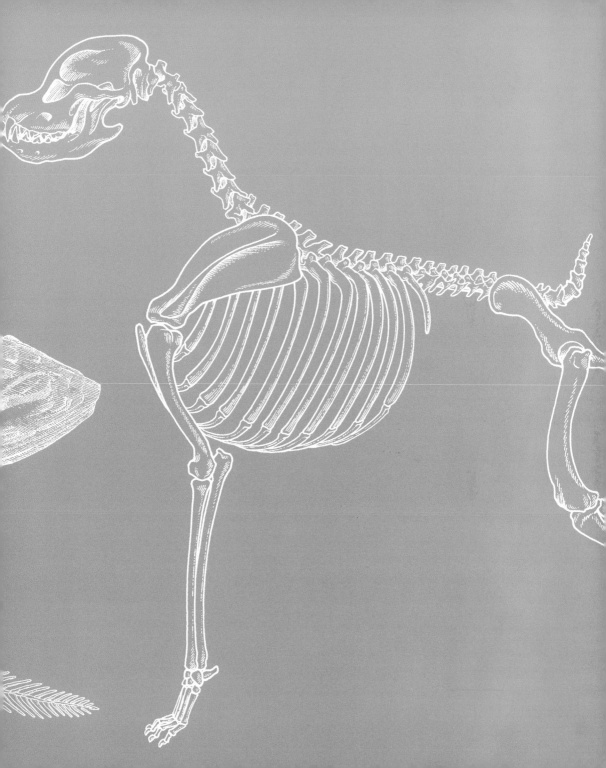

ANCIENT
TO MODERN

The lamprey is an elongated, eel-like animal with one long dorsal fin toward its tail but no pectoral or ventral fins. It has a spine and skull, below, but no ribs.

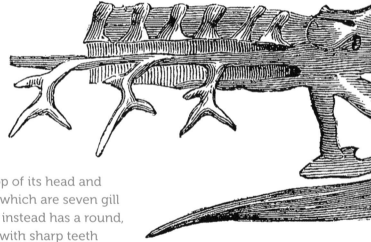

There is a single nostril on top of its head and laterally placed eyes, behind which are seven gill openings. It has no jaws, but instead has a round, sucker-like mouth equipped with sharp teeth which it uses to attach itself to its prey before burrowing into it to suck its blood.

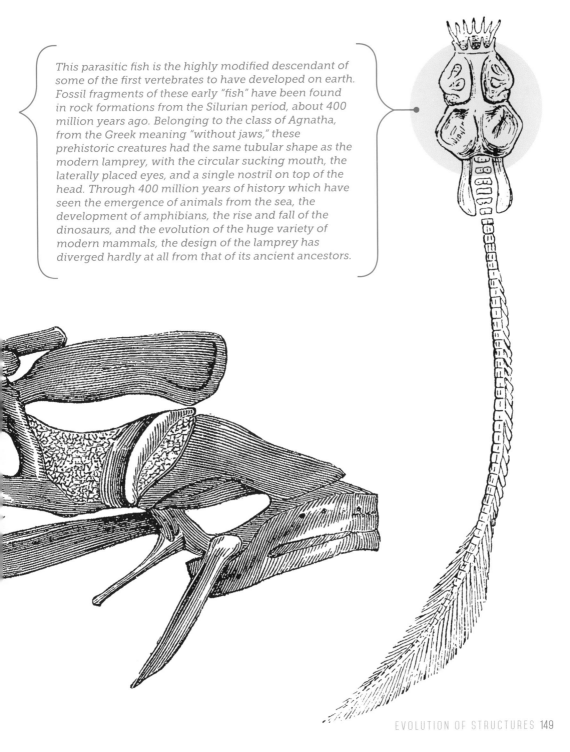

This parasitic fish is the highly modified descendant of some of the first vertebrates to have developed on earth. Fossil fragments of these early "fish" have been found in rock formations from the Silurian period, about 400 million years ago. Belonging to the class of Agnatha, from the Greek meaning "without jaws," these prehistoric creatures had the same tubular shape as the modern lamprey, with the circular sucking mouth, the laterally placed eyes, and a single nostril on top of the head. Through 400 million years of history which have seen the emergence of animals from the sea, the development of amphibians, the rise and fall of the dinosaurs, and the evolution of the huge variety of modern mammals, the design of the lamprey has diverged hardly at all from that of its ancient ancestors.

FOSSILS

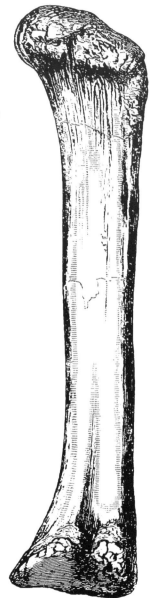

Evidence for the evolution of skeletal structures comes from the study of fossils, the remains of long-dead animals preserved in the earth's sedimentary rocks. These are usually the hard parts of the body, such as the bones and teeth, which may be petrified—that is, turned into stone—or may be preserved in their original state. It was discovered in the nineteenth century that particular fossil assemblages were always found together and therefore that particular rock layers could be dated to the same period. Eventually, a chronology of prehistoric eras was established, which was then further subdivided into periods and epochs, until enough evidence had been gathered to enable us to piece together a history of life on earth.

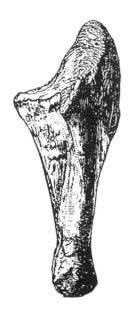
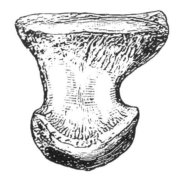
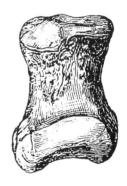

Working out the shape of an animal and its relationships with other animals from its remains depends to some degree on analogies from what we know of the structure of modern animals. The size of the bones will indicate the scale of the animal. The bones will have processes for muscle attachment, and the size of these indicates the strength of the muscles, which in turn would suggest how the bone moved. The ends of jointed bones will show how one bone moved relative to its neighbor.

Fixing the position of the animal in the evolutionary matrix depends on identifying shared characteristics and then establishing which ones are significant enough to identify animals as belonging to one family rather than another. Often the picture of an ancient animal has to be put together from very few pieces of actual evidence, but the fossil record is now so well established that most new discoveries fill in gaps that have already been predicted rather than producing any shocks.

DEVELOPMENT
OF JAWS

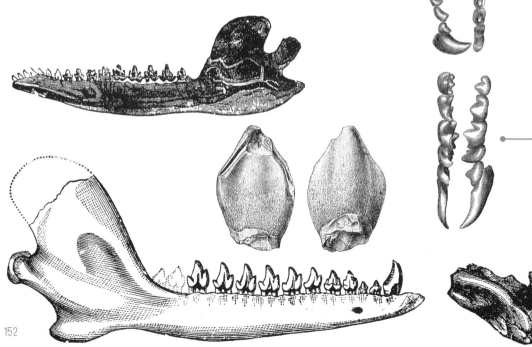

The chronological sequence of fossils can be established from
the rocks in which they are found, so a progression from one
group to the next can be drawn up. General patterns of skeletal
evolution over time include such things as a reduction in the
number of separate bones, particularly the bones of the feet
and skull, and specialization of teeth.

The development of jaw structures marks significant boundaries between different animal groups. In early fish the upper jaw or palatoquadrate was connected with the cranium at the front and the back. As jaws evolved, the palatoquadrate became articulated only at the front, so that it could slide forward and increase the size of the gape. This is called the hyostylic condition and is the jaw found in most modern fish.

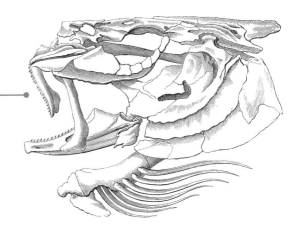

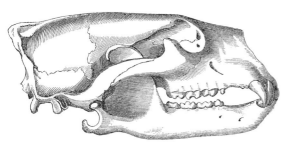

Teeth and jaws are of particular interest, partly because teeth, being the hardest parts of the skeleton, are those most often preserved. From the shape and size of the teeth of a skeleton a paleontologist can tell what it ate, how big it was, even which animal family it belonged to and whereabouts in the evolutionary development of that family it falls.

In the earliest land animals the palatoquadrate became fused to the cranium, the autostylic condition characteristic of the tetrapods, the first four-limbed vertebrates and all their descendants. Other changes involved the way the lower jaw was hinged. In the earliest animals the lower jaw was attached via several bones, but over time the number of bones reduced. In modern reptiles such as the crocodile, the hinge is made up of two bones, but the mammal jaw, as in the polar bear, is hinged directly to the cranium. The bones that formerly made up the jaw connection grew smaller and migrated to become the ossicles that transmit sounds to the inner ear.

BONY FISH

Bony fish with jaws are known from the late Silurian period and started to diversify in the late Devonian. They can be divided into two groups: "ray-finned" fish whose fins are supported by thin bony rods, and "lobe-finned" fish, whose fins have a more substantial basal bone.

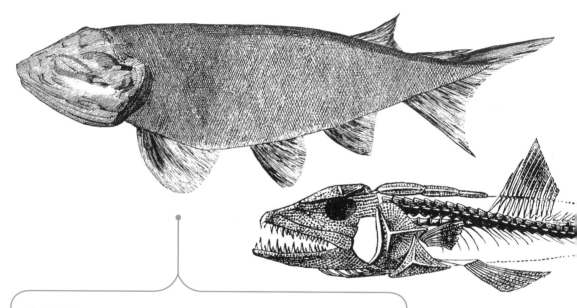

Cheirolepis, top, was a robust fish from the late Devonian period. Its body was covered with tiny bony scales and its tail fin is longer at the top than at the bottom, a characteristic of very early fish skeletons. Eurypholis, middle, from the later Cretaceous period was a predator equipped with rows of sharp teeth. It had a tall dorsal fin and a symmetrical tail. Leptolepis, right, was one of the first modern fish and first appeared in the Jurassic period. It had a single dorsal fin, a symmetrical tail fin, and a shorter jaw than its predecessors. From this basic form evolved the huge range of shapes and sizes of fish known today.

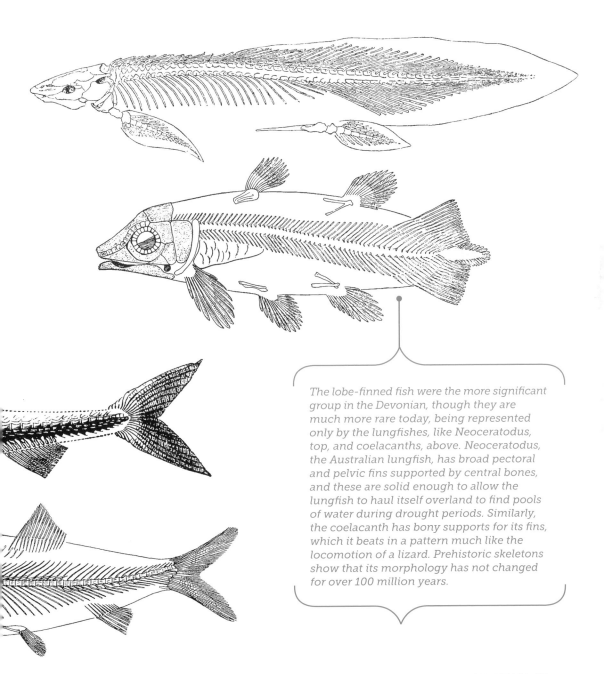

The lobe-finned fish were the more significant group in the Devonian, though they are much more rare today, being represented only by the lungfishes, like Neoceratodus, top, and coelacanths, above. Neoceratodus, the Australian lungfish, has broad pectoral and pelvic fins supported by central bones, and these are solid enough to allow the lungfish to haul itself overland to find pools of water during drought periods. Similarly, the coelacanth has bony supports for its fins, which it beats in a pattern much like the locomotion of a lizard. Prehistoric skeletons show that its morphology has not changed for over 100 million years.

SHARKS

The sharks were the other main group apart
from bony fish that emerged after the jawless fish
in the Devonian period. Sharks had, and still have, a
cartilaginous rather than a bony skeleton, though the
spinal cord in modern sharks is calcified, which helps
them to resist compressive forces during rapid
swimming. An early shark, Cladoselache from the
late Devonian period, is known from a very well-
preserved fossil. It looked much like a modern
shark, with the familiar torpedo shape, pairs of
pectoral and pelvic fins and two dorsal fins,
and six gill slits.

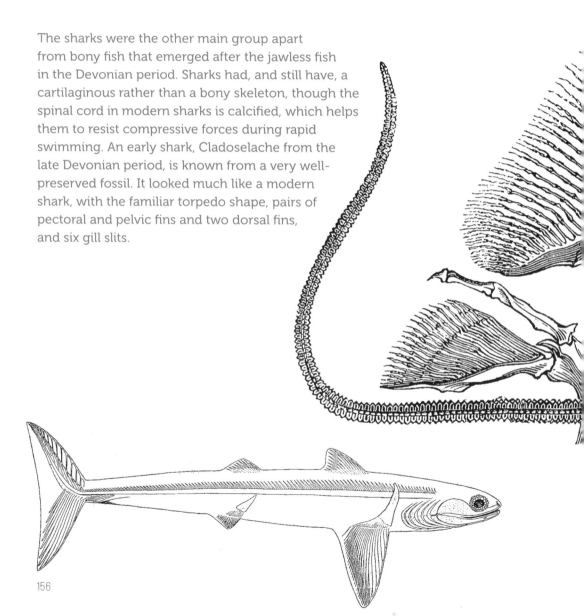

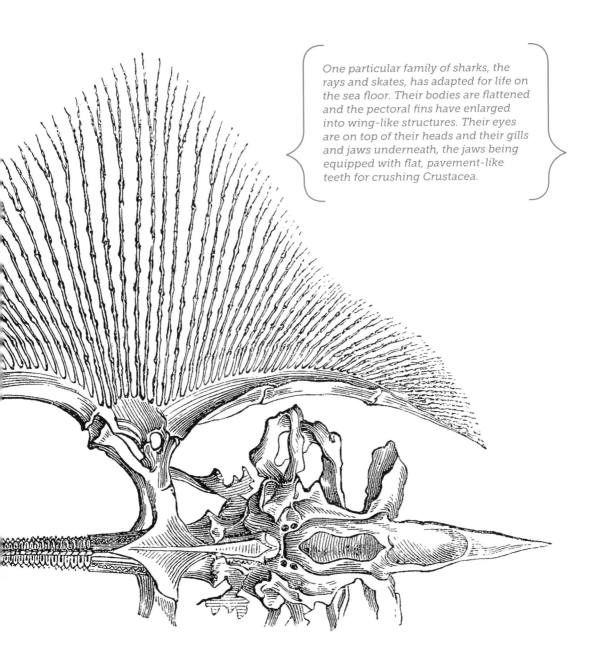

One particular family of sharks, the rays and skates, has adapted for life on the sea floor. Their bodies are flattened and the pectoral fins have enlarged into wing-like structures. Their eyes are on top of their heads and their gills and jaws underneath, the jaws being equipped with flat, pavement-like teeth for crushing Crustacea.

TETRAPOD DEVELOPMENT

Eusthenopteron, right, was a lobe-finned fish from the late Devonian period. It was about 3 feet (1 m) long, with a three-lobed tail fin and jaws equipped with sharp teeth. Its skeleton has a number of adaptations that point the way toward animals that would be able to move around on land. It had a well-developed spine, an essential feature for an animal to be able to support itself without the buoyancy of water. The pectoral fins, far right, had the three bones that form the upper forelimbs of modern tetrapods – the humerus, radius, and ulna – and the beginnings of the wrist bones. The pelvic fins similarly have the upper bones of the hind limbs. Eusthenopteron would not have been able to walk properly on land, but its skeleton does have some key features that would develop in that direction.

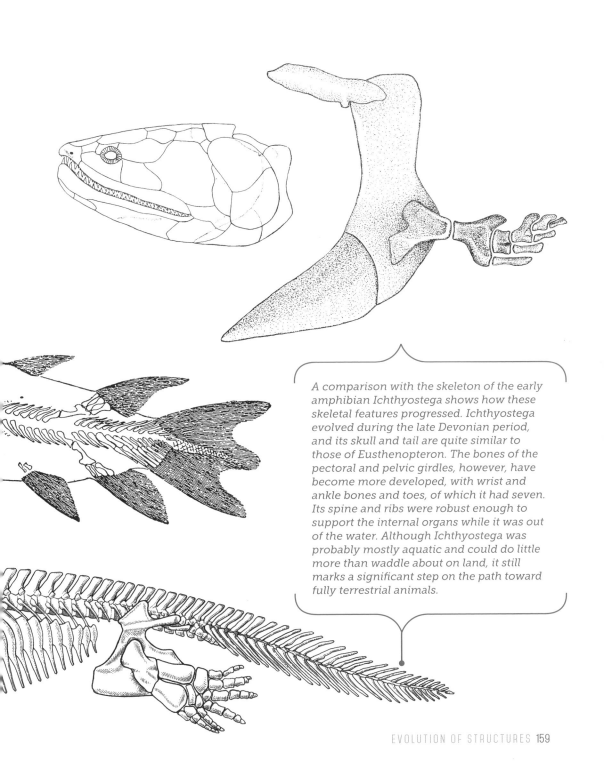

A comparison with the skeleton of the early amphibian Ichthyostega shows how these skeletal features progressed. Ichthyostega evolved during the late Devonian period, and its skull and tail are quite similar to those of Eusthenopteron. The bones of the pectoral and pelvic girdles, however, have become more developed, with wrist and ankle bones and toes, of which it had seven. Its spine and ribs were robust enough to support the internal organs while it was out of the water. Although Ichthyostega was probably mostly aquatic and could do little more than waddle about on land, it still marks a significant step on the path toward fully terrestrial animals.

TERRESTRIAL AMPHIBIANS

Seymouria was an amphibian that lived during the early Permian period. Its skeleton has moved on a long way from that of Ichthyostega in terms of adapting to life on land. The spine is strong with pronounced processes for muscle attachment, and the ribs are narrower and less bladelike. The pelvic girdle is substantial, to form a strong anchor for the rear limbs, and the caudal vertebrae have lost their fin rays. The pectoral girdle is separated further from the back of the skull, allowing greater neck mobility. The upper bones of the legs are more elongated, as are the bones of the fingers and toes, and these have reduced in number to five. Its longer legs would have meant that Seymouria could hold itself up off the ground instead of waddling along on its belly. Its legs project sideways from its body, so it would have moved like a modern lizard, swinging its body from side to side to increase the length of its limbs.

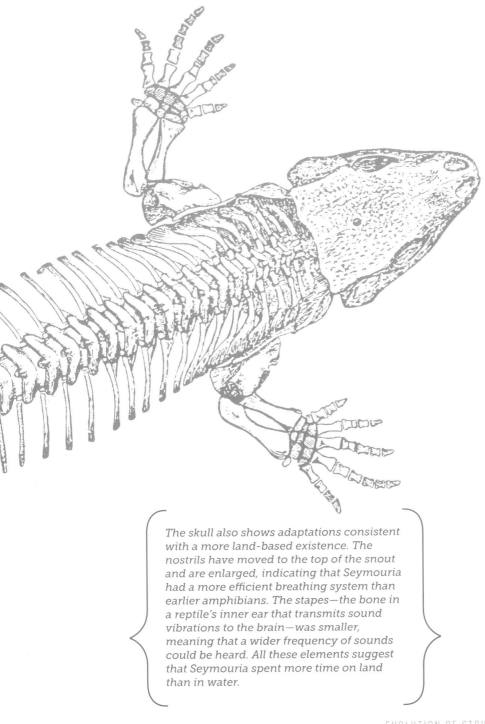

The skull also shows adaptations consistent with a more land-based existence. The nostrils have moved to the top of the snout and are enlarged, indicating that Seymouria had a more efficient breathing system than earlier amphibians. The stapes—the bone in a reptile's inner ear that transmits sound vibrations to the brain—was smaller, meaning that a wider frequency of sounds could be heard. All these elements suggest that Seymouria spent more time on land than in water.

MAMMAL- LIKE REPTILES

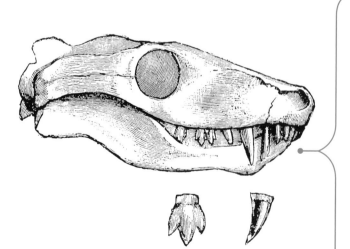

Skulls and teeth are important indicators when it comes to establishing patterns of skeletal evolution. All modern reptiles are diapsids, which means that they have 2 holes in the skull behind the eye orbits. Modern mammals are synapsids, having only one post-orbital gap in their skulls. However, there was a group of ancient synapsid reptiles. Fossils of these reptiles, the therapsids, have been found from the late Permian to the Jurassic period, by which stage their skeletons were very close in organization to those of mammals, which suggests that these reptiles at some point gave rise to the first mammals.

Galesaurus was thought to be a dinosaur when first discovered but is in fact a member of the cynodont group, as is Cynognathus, top. Their teeth were differentiated into incisors, canines, and cusped cheek teeth; the bones at the back of the lower jaw that articulated with the skull were greatly reduced, more in line with the mammalian mandible, which is a single bone articulating directly with the upper jaw; and there was a bony palate at the roof of the mouth separating it from the nasal passages. All of these features are characteristic of the skeletons of mammals.

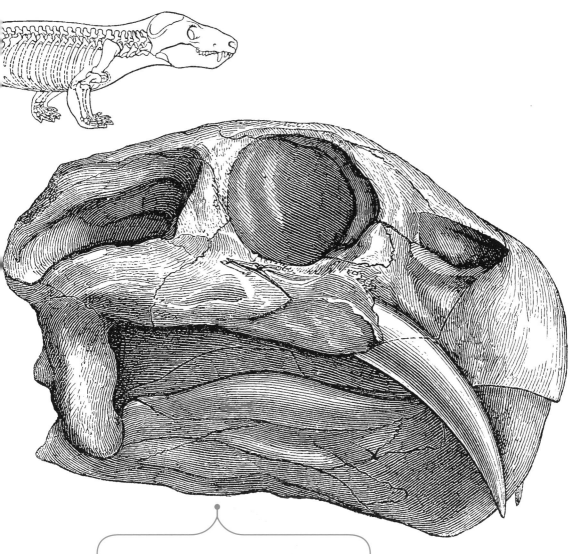

Dicynodon was a very widespread mammal-like reptile during the Permian period. Its skull had a large gap behind the eye and pronounced tusklike canine teeth in the upper jaw. Dicynodon had no other teeth apart from these, which may have been used for digging up roots and insects or possibly for display. It had a horny beak and was about 4 feet (1.2 m) long.

ARCHAEOPTERYX

Archaeopteryx is justifiably one of the most iconic ancient animals, representing as it does a classic "missing link" in evolutionary development. It is known from 10 fossil specimens from the late Jurassic period, some of which are complete skeletons with impressions of feathers.

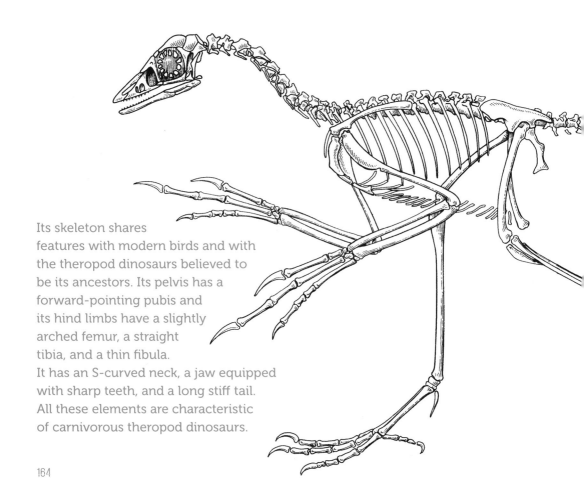

Its skeleton shares features with modern birds and with the theropod dinosaurs believed to be its ancestors. Its pelvis has a forward-pointing pubis and its hind limbs have a slightly arched femur, a straight tibia, and a thin fibula.
It has an S-curved neck, a jaw equipped with sharp teeth, and a long stiff tail. All these elements are characteristic of carnivorous theropod dinosaurs.

The forelimbs of Archaeopteryx approach those of modern birds. The shoulder girdle has a long, narrow scapula and short coracoid, with a bony sternum attaching the coracoids, although this lacks the keel that provides a firm anchor for the wings in modern birds. The forelimbs are greatly extended, with three long fingers to which the primary flight feathers are attached. Secondary feathers, attached to the ulna, are protected by covert feathers just as in modern birds. The eyes are large and so is the brain case, indicating that the brain was sufficiently advanced to cope with the complexities of flying. This animal was a striking example of evolutionary adaptation.

EARLY
MAMMALS

Mammals emerged in Triassic times, developing from the various mammal-like reptiles to establish distinctive defining characteristics such as a body covering of hair instead of scales, a constant body temperature, and giving birth to live young rather than laying eggs. Defining skeletal features of mammals include the bony palate, differentiation of teeth, a lower jaw consisting of a single fused bone, and an enlarged brain case.

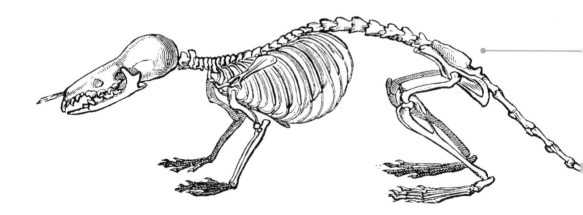

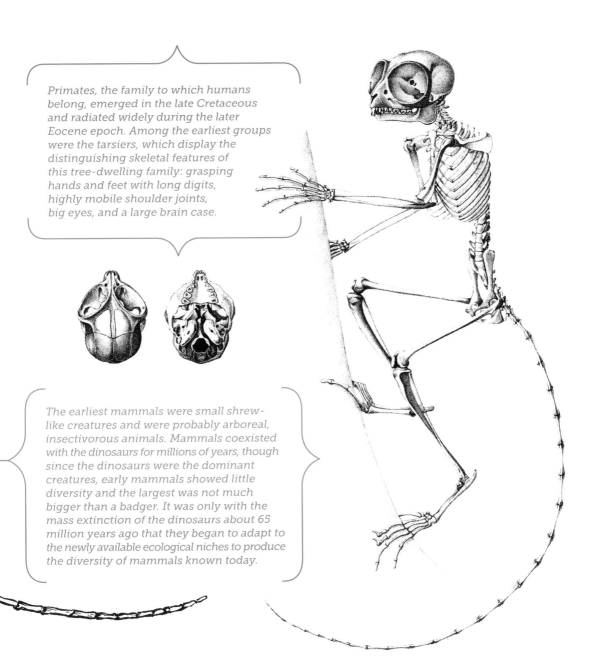

Primates, the family to which humans belong, emerged in the late Cretaceous and radiated widely during the later Eocene epoch. Among the earliest groups were the tarsiers, which display the distinguishing skeletal features of this tree-dwelling family: grasping hands and feet with long digits, highly mobile shoulder joints, big eyes, and a large brain case.

The earliest mammals were small shrew-like creatures and were probably arboreal, insectivorous animals. Mammals coexisted with the dinosaurs for millions of years, though since the dinosaurs were the dominant creatures, early mammals showed little diversity and the largest was not much bigger than a badger. It was only with the mass extinction of the dinosaurs about 65 million years ago that they began to adapt to the newly available ecological niches to produce the diversity of mammals known today.

MARSUPIALS

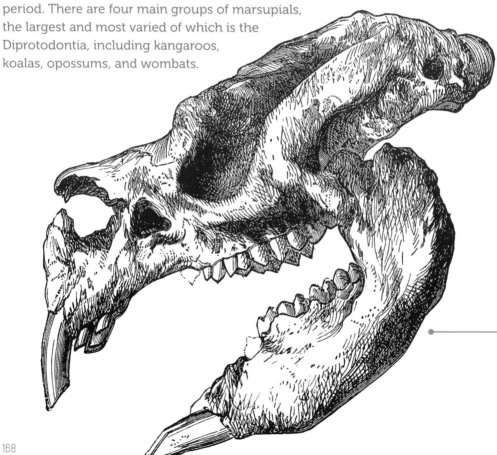

Fossils of marsupials, in which the young are nursed for some time after birth in their mother's pouch, are first found in late Cretaceous rocks in North America, though it is possible that they originated in Asia. They dispersed southward through South America to Australia, where they uniquely flourished as a result of this island continent's isolation from other land masses from the beginning of the Tertiary period. There are four main groups of marsupials, the largest and most varied of which is the Diprotodontia, including kangaroos, koalas, opossums, and wombats.

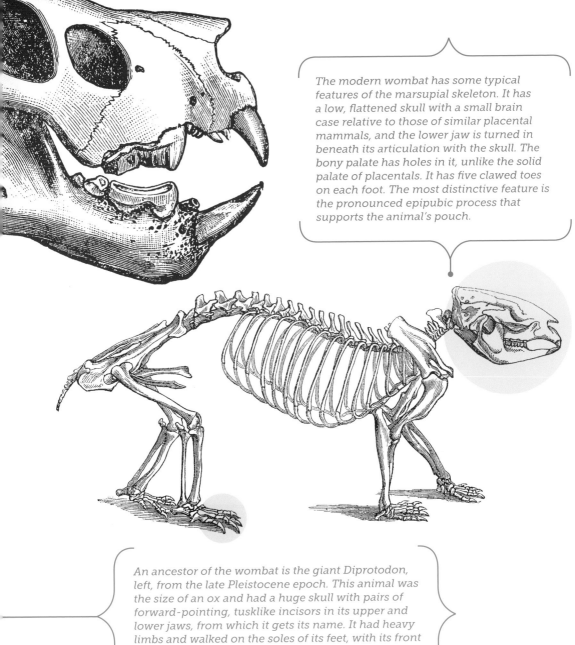

The modern wombat has some typical features of the marsupial skeleton. It has a low, flattened skull with a small brain case relative to those of similar placental mammals, and the lower jaw is turned in beneath its articulation with the skull. The bony palate has holes in it, unlike the solid palate of placentals. It has five clawed toes on each foot. The most distinctive feature is the pronounced epipubic process that supports the animal's pouch.

An ancestor of the wombat is the giant Diprotodon, left, from the late Pleistocene epoch. This animal was the size of an ox and had a huge skull with pairs of forward-pointing, tusklike incisors in its upper and lower jaws, from which it gets its name. It had heavy limbs and walked on the soles of its feet, with its front legs turned inward. Another Pleistocene diprotodont was the carnivorous marsupial "lion," Thylacoleo, top center, which had sharp, pointed incisors and shearing, bladelike cheek teeth.

HORNS

The bovids are a family of animals that belong to the larger group of artiodactyls, or even-toed hoofed animals. They are important for humans because they include cattle, sheep, and goats, animals which have supplied us with resources for thousands of years. A distinguishing characteristic of bovids is the possession of horns, which come in an amazing variety of shapes and sizes. Horns consist of bony outgrowths of the frontal bones sheathed in keratin. They probably evolved as defensive structures, just as they had in the Ceratopsia family of dinosaurs millions of years before, a good example of convergent evolution whereby similar structures arise in different places and at different times via different routes. Horns range from short spikes to long lances, and they can be straight, curved, fluted, or twisted.

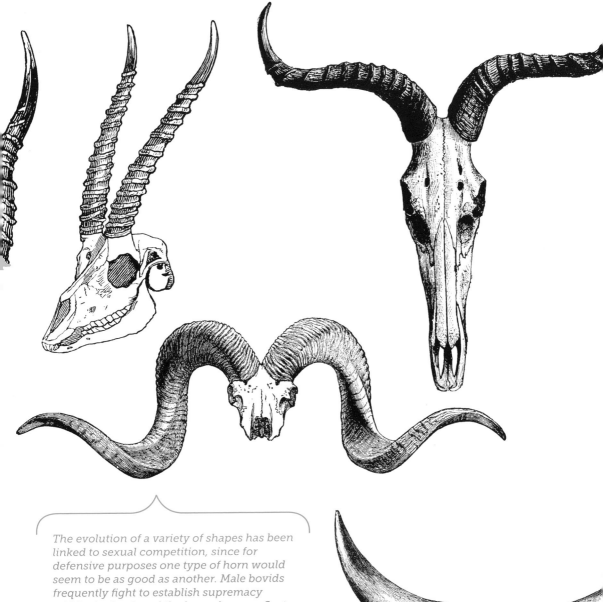

The evolution of a variety of shapes has been linked to sexual competition, since for defensive purposes one type of horn would seem to be as good as another. Male bovids frequently fight to establish supremacy within the herd, and the horn shapes reflect the way the animals fight, whether wrestling, fencing, or butting. The greater the degree of competition for females, the larger and more elaborate the horns. Equally, monogamous and solitary antelopes, such as duikers, have small horns.

GRAVITY

The size of an animal is governed by a number of factors, including population density, food supply, and climate. With regard to skeletons, a key factor is gravity. In the seventeenth century Galileo pointed out that the weight of a body is the cube of its linear dimension, whether height or width. This means that an animal's weight increases at a faster rate than its size.

The strength of a bone, however, is governed by its cross-sectional area, that is, the square of the linear dimension. This means that the bigger an animal is, the more of its body has to be taken up by the bony structure that supports its weight. So bones make up 8 percent of the body of a mouse, opposite, top left, 13 percent of the body of a dog, opposite, top right, and 18 percent of the body of a human, right.

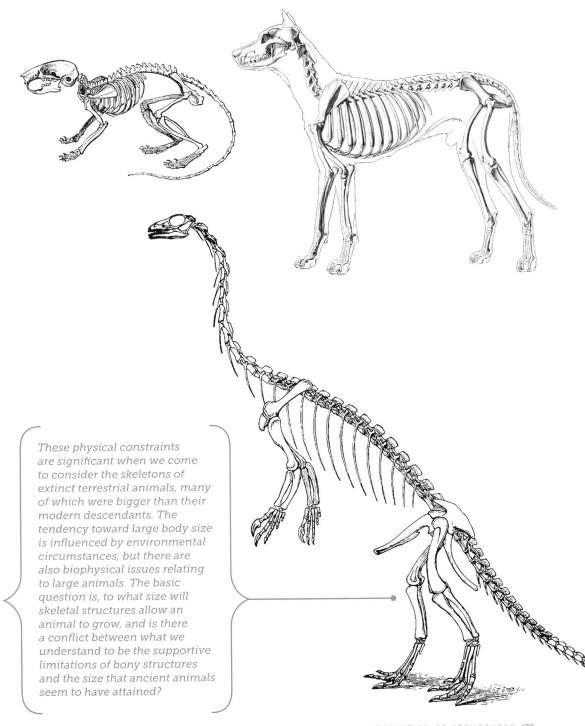

These physical constraints are significant when we come to consider the skeletons of extinct terrestrial animals, many of which were bigger than their modern descendants. The tendency toward large body size is influenced by environmental circumstances, but there are also biophysical issues relating to large animals. The basic question is, to what size will skeletal structures allow an animal to grow, and is there a conflict between what we understand to be the supportive limitations of bony structures and the size that ancient animals seem to have attained?

AIR & WATER

The male African elephant stands about 13 feet (4 m) tall and weighs around 7 tons (6.35 metric tons). The size of the elephant is a trade-off between the constraints of bone strength relative to weight and the need to be able to function: to move, eat, reproduce, and defend itself from predators. The force of gravity acting on the elephant is such that its bones have to do a huge amount of work to support it and move it around.

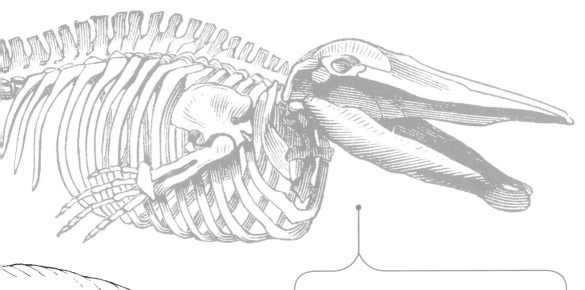

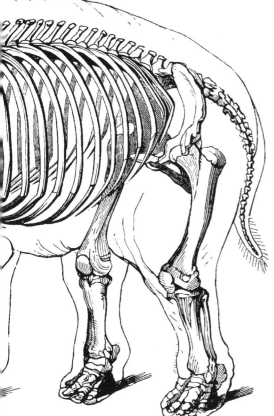

The largest aquatic animal, the blue whale, can be as much as 100 feet (30 m) long and weigh up to 160 tons (145 metric tons). It is the biggest creature ever known, bigger even than any dinosaur. The blue whale weighs about 20 times as much as the elephant, and yet its skeleton forms a smaller percentage of its bodyweight. The key term here is weight, since in the zero G environment of the sea the whale is effectively weightless. The difference in the forces acting on the whale and the elephant is evident from the proportion of their bodies taken up by bone. The whale's skeleton is maintaining its shape, but the job of supporting its mass is done by the water around it. Without the constraints of gravity, the whale can reach an enormous size with the same type of bony structure. But if the whale is unfortunate enough to get stranded on the beach, it will literally be crushed to death by its own weight.

GIANTISM

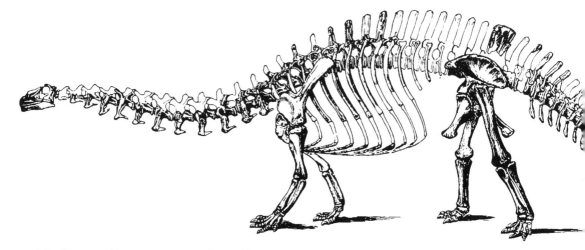

The largest dinosaurs were about five times the size of the largest modern terrestrial animals. Apatosaurus, above, one of the biggest herbivorous dinosaurs from the late Jurassic and early Cretaceous period, was about 80 feet (24 m) long, most of which was neck and tail. Iguanadon, far right, from the same period, was about 30 feet (9 m) long. Pterosaur skeletons, right, have been found with wingspans of about 50 feet (15 m), as compared to the 12-foot (3.5-m) wingspan of the largest modern bird, the wandering albatross.

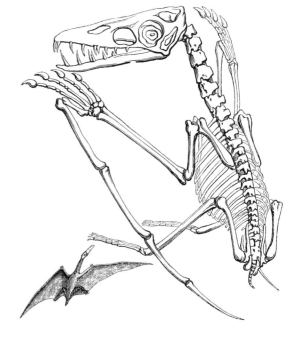

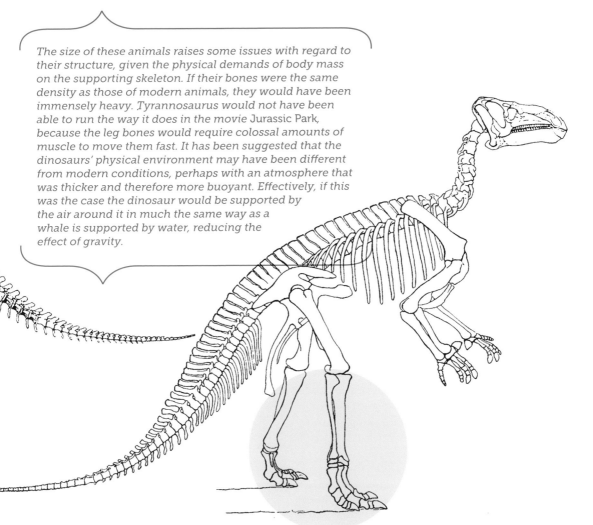

The size of these animals raises some issues with regard to their structure, given the physical demands of body mass on the supporting skeleton. If their bones were the same density as those of modern animals, they would have been immensely heavy. *Tyrannosaurus* would not have been able to run the way it does in the movie *Jurassic Park*, because the leg bones would require colossal amounts of muscle to move them fast. It has been suggested that the dinosaurs' physical environment may have been different from modern conditions, perhaps with an atmosphere that was thicker and therefore more buoyant. Effectively, if this was the case the dinosaur would be supported by the air around it in much the same way as a whale is supported by water, reducing the effect of gravity.

A more plausible explanation is that dinosaur bones contained air sacs, like the bones of birds, which helped with respiration but also reduced the animal's weight without sacrificing bone strength. This would allow them to grow to a greater size than modern animals. Nonetheless, there remain many questions about how animals of this scale could have functioned.

HUMAN DEVELOPMENT

Two distinctive characteristics radically separate humans from other apes: bipedalism and large brain size. Which happened first was a matter of some controversy during the early years of paleontology in the mid-nineteenth century, but it is now generally accepted that humans got up on their hind legs about 6 million years ago, while evidence for increasing brain size begins about 2 million years ago.

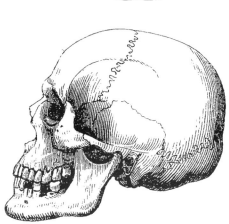

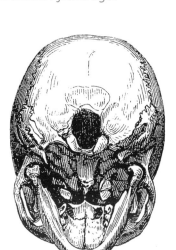

Both of these characteristics are reflected in human skulls. Walking upright means that the skull is balanced on top of the spine, which means in turn that the foramen magnum, the opening through which the spinal cord passes, is further forward in humans than in other apes, almost directly under the dome of the skull. This key signifier allows prehistoric hominid skulls to be identified accurately even from relatively small pieces of bone, as long as the position of the foramen magnum can be established.

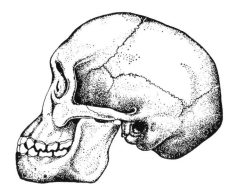

Increasing brain size in evolving humans also had an effect on the skull. These changes can be clearly seen in the progression from Australopithecus (top, late Pliocene) through Homo erectus (center, early Pleistocene) to Homo neanderthalis (bottom, late Pleistocene). The back of the skull became enlarged and the forehead grew higher and more dome-like. The projecting face of the apes was flattened by this enlarging brain case, so that the face was underneath the front part of the brain. This also reduced the space for the teeth, so they formed a continuous arc without the gap between the incisors and the canines that is found in apes.

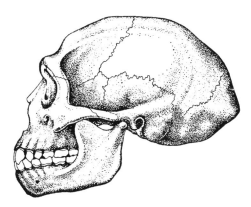

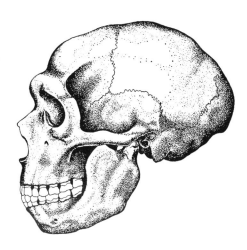

DOMESTIC HORSES

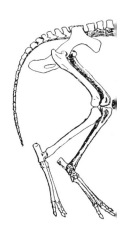

Domestication involves controlling the behavior and breeding of an animal to suit the specific purposes of humans. Indicators of domestication in the fossil record are such things as the sudden arrival of a new species in a particular location, suggesting that it has been introduced deliberately; an increase in numbers of particular species relative to other species, suggesting that their breeding and survival is being encouraged; and morphological changes, indicating that animals are being bred for specific features. It is now possible to examine the DNA of prehistoric remains to uncover evidence of selective breeding.

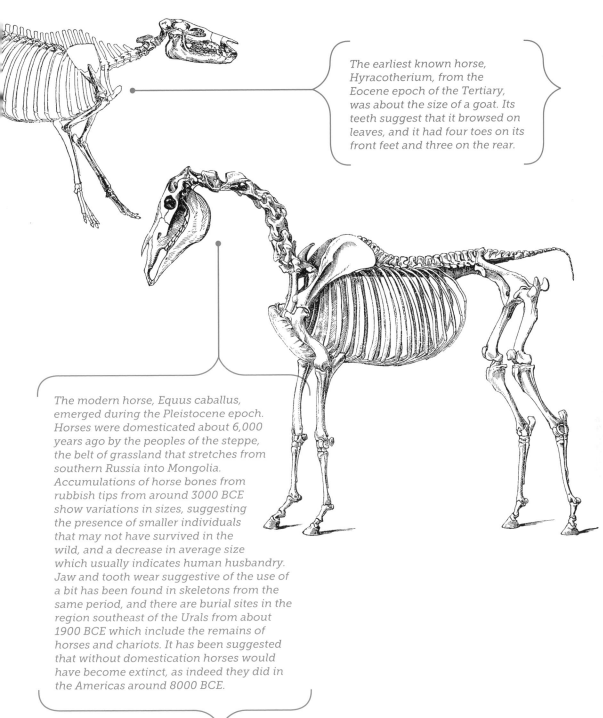

The earliest known horse, *Hyracotherium*, from the Eocene epoch of the Tertiary, was about the size of a goat. Its teeth suggest that it browsed on leaves, and it had four toes on its front feet and three on the rear.

The modern horse, *Equus caballus*, emerged during the Pleistocene epoch. Horses were domesticated about 6,000 years ago by the peoples of the steppe, the belt of grassland that stretches from southern Russia into Mongolia. Accumulations of horse bones from rubbish tips from around 3000 BCE show variations in sizes, suggesting the presence of smaller individuals that may not have survived in the wild, and a decrease in average size which usually indicates human husbandry. Jaw and tooth wear suggestive of the use of a bit has been found in skeletons from the same period, and there are burial sites in the region southeast of the Urals from about 1900 BCE which include the remains of horses and chariots. It has been suggested that without domestication horses would have become extinct, as indeed they did in the Americas around 8000 BCE.

CONTROLLED BREEDING

Dogs were the first animals to be domesticated by humans, about 12,000 years ago, almost certainly to help with hunting. The ancestor of the modern dog is the wolf, a hunting pack animal whose lifestyle can easily be imagined to fit with that of prehistoric hunter-gatherers. There are over 400 different modern breeds of dog—from the robust boxer, top right, to the short-legged dachshund, below right—and the process of selective breeding that has produced this variety basically demonstrates evolution speeded up. Where evolutionary processes select particular body shapes and sizes in response to the optimum exploitation of a particular ecological niche, selective breeding performs the same action on the basis of human requirements. Hunting dogs such as greyhounds have been developed for speed, others such as beagles for their ability to hunt by scent. Small hunting dogs like terriers and dachshunds have been bred to be able to enter underground burrows, while guard dogs are usually large and intimidating. Some breeds are highly specialized, such as the Newfoundland, a large powerful dog with a robust skeleton, a thick oily coat, and webbed paws which make it an excellent ocean swimmer.

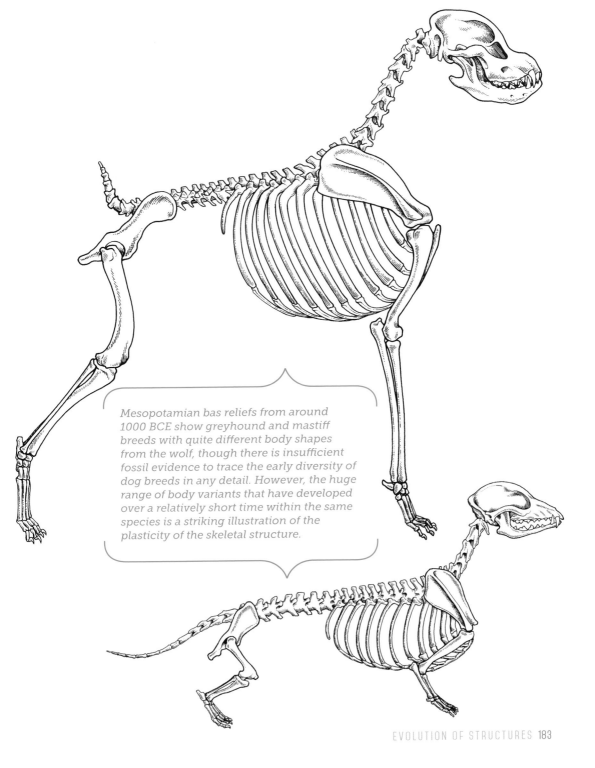

Mesopotamian bas reliefs from around
1000 BCE show greyhound and mastiff
breeds with quite different body shapes
from the wolf, though there is insufficient
fossil evidence to trace the early diversity of
dog breeds in any detail. However, the huge
range of body variants that have developed
over a relatively short time within the same
species is a striking illustration of the
plasticity of the skeletal structure.

ANCIENT ANIMALS

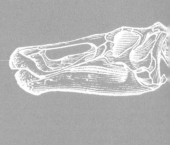

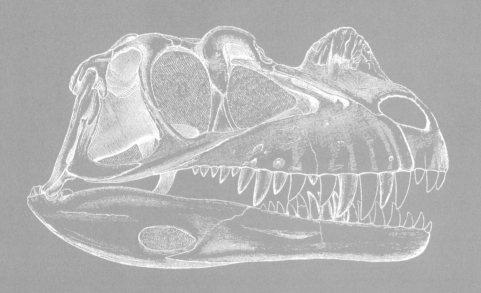

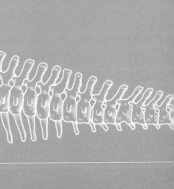

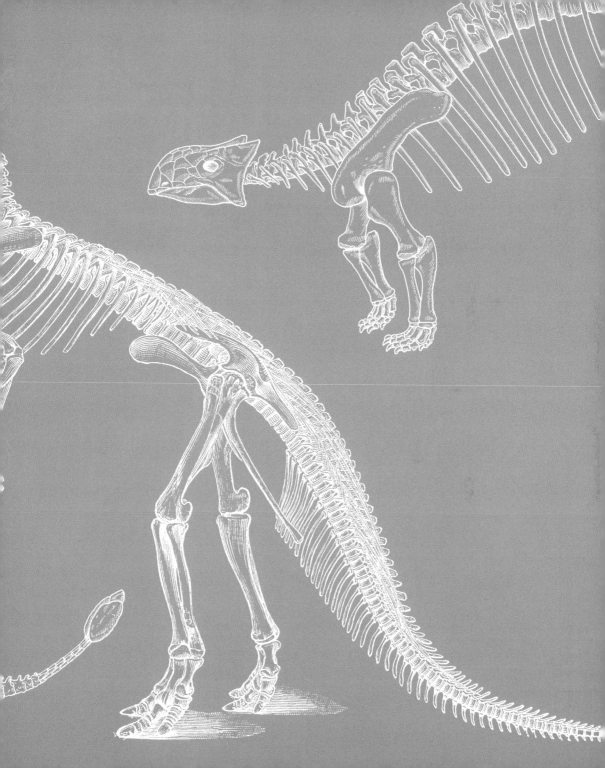

DINOSAURS

Dinosaurs are conventionally divided into two main groups, based on two distinctive pelvic structures. The Saurischia or "lizard-hipped" dinosaurs have a triangular pelvis, with the pubis pointing forward and the ischium backward. This more primitive structure can be found in the carnivorous theropods and the herbivorous sauropodomorphs.

The Ornithischia or "bird-hipped" dinosaurs have a more elongated pelvis in which the pubis and the ischium are both aligned backward, with an additional pre-pubic process at the front. All herbivores, the group is comprised of four main families: the bipedal ornithopods and the quadruped, armored stegosaurs, ankylosaurs, and ceratopsians.

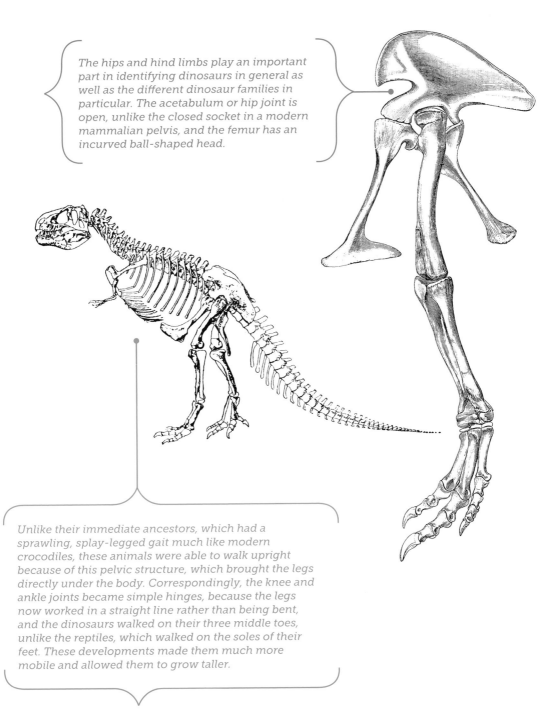

The hips and hind limbs play an important part in identifying dinosaurs in general as well as the different dinosaur families in particular. The acetabulum or hip joint is open, unlike the closed socket in a modern mammalian pelvis, and the femur has an incurved ball-shaped head.

Unlike their immediate ancestors, which had a sprawling, splay-legged gait much like modern crocodiles, these animals were able to walk upright because of this pelvic structure, which brought the legs directly under the body. Correspondingly, the knee and ankle joints became simple hinges, because the legs now worked in a straight line rather than being bent, and the dinosaurs walked on their three middle toes, unlike the reptiles, which walked on the soles of their feet. These developments made them much more mobile and allowed them to grow taller.

SAURISCHIAN THEROPODS

Ceratosaurus was a carnivorous, saurischian theropod dinosaur from the Jurassic period, a relative of the huge carnivores such as Tyrannosaurus and Allosaurus. Its fossil remains have been found in deposits in Utah and Colorado. It was about 18 feet (5.5 m) long with a relatively large skull compared with other theropods, and its jaws were equipped with sharp, bladelike teeth. It had a prominent horn on the top of its nose and two more above its eyes, which were probably used for sexual display to attract a mate. It also had a bony crest running down its spine. Its forelimbs were robust, though quite short, and had four fingers on each hand, denoting a relatively primitive condition.

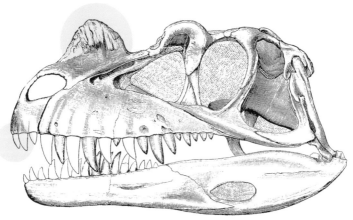
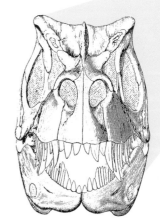

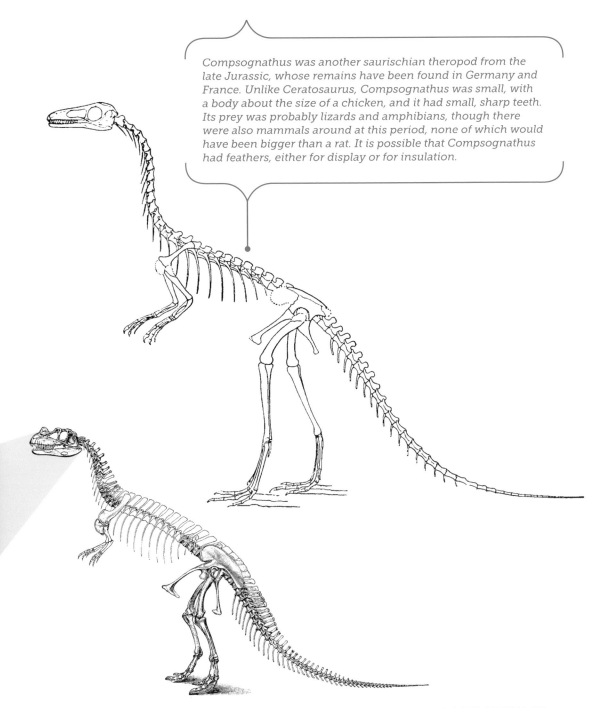

Compsognathus was another saurischian theropod from the late Jurassic, whose remains have been found in Germany and France. Unlike Ceratosaurus, Compsognathus was small, with a body about the size of a chicken, and it had small, sharp teeth. Its prey was probably lizards and amphibians, though there were also mammals around at this period, none of which would have been bigger than a rat. It is possible that Compsognathus had feathers, either for display or for insulation.

SAUROPODO- MORPHS

The second group of saurischian dinosaurs, the sauropodomorphs, are the giant plant-eaters familiar from natural history museums all over the world. Their skeletons are characterized by long necks with elongated cervical vertebrae numbering 12 or more, robust, pillar-like limbs with greatly reduced phalanges to support their weight, and highly pneumatized vertebrae. Camarasaurus, above, was a member of the Macronaria, a family of dinosaurs that share a distinctive, boxy skull shape, with a broad, square snout and very large nasal cavities just in front of the eyes. It has been suggested that these enlarged nostrils may have had some kind of cooling function for the skull. The skull itself is small and made up of bony arches with large gaps between them to reduce weight. The forelimbs of Macronaria species are often longer than the hind limbs, suggesting that it browsed on high-growing vegetation.

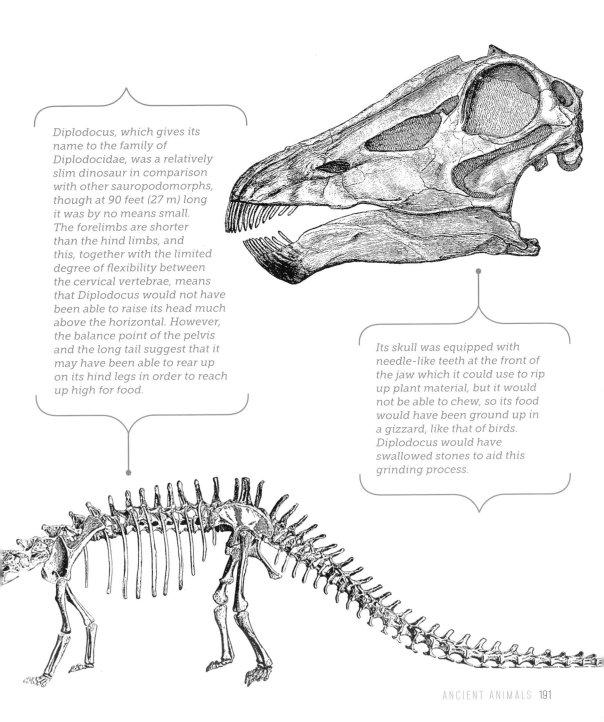

Diplodocus, which gives its name to the family of Diplodocidae, was a relatively slim dinosaur in comparison with other sauropodomorphs, though at 90 feet (27 m) long it was by no means small. The forelimbs are shorter than the hind limbs, and this, together with the limited degree of flexibility between the cervical vertebrae, means that Diplodocus would not have been able to raise its head much above the horizontal. However, the balance point of the pelvis and the long tail suggest that it may have been able to rear up on its hind legs in order to reach up high for food.

Its skull was equipped with needle-like teeth at the front of the jaw which it could use to rip up plant material, but it would not be able to chew, so its food would have been ground up in a gizzard, like that of birds. Diplodocus would have swallowed stones to aid this grinding process.

ORNITHOPODS

The ornithopods began as small grazing dinosaurs and evolved into highly successful, large herbivores. Their name means "bird-footed." Hypsilophodon, below, was a bipedal herbivorous dinosaur, about 7 feet (2 m) long from nose to tail. Its skeleton clearly shows the backward-pointing pubis and ischium which identify it as a member of the ornithischian group. Its back legs were long and there were three main toes on each foot. These features, together with the pattern of musculature around the thigh and hip bones, indicate that it was a fast-running dinosaur. The end of its tail was stiffened with ossified tendons, meaning that it could hold it out straight as a stabilizer while it was running.

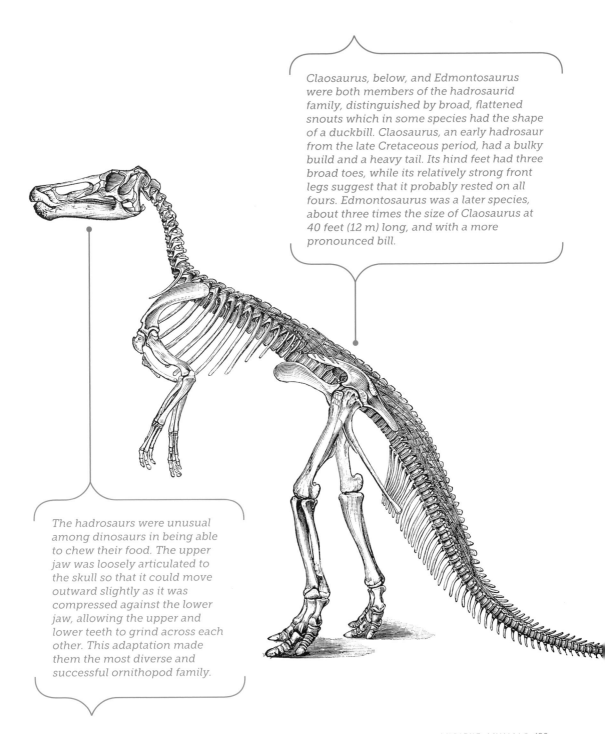

Claosaurus, below, and Edmontosaurus were both members of the hadrosaurid family, distinguished by broad, flattened snouts which in some species had the shape of a duckbill. Claosaurus, an early hadrosaur from the late Cretaceous period, had a bulky build and a heavy tail. Its hind feet had three broad toes, while its relatively strong front legs suggest that it probably rested on all fours. Edmontosaurus was a later species, about three times the size of Claosaurus at 40 feet (12 m) long, and with a more pronounced bill.

The hadrosaurs were unusual among dinosaurs in being able to chew their food. The upper jaw was loosely articulated to the skull so that it could move outward slightly as it was compressed against the lower jaw, allowing the upper and lower teeth to grind across each other. This adaptation made them the most diverse and successful ornithopod family.

STEGOSAURS

The other major group of ornithischian dinosaurs were the armored dinosaurs that began to appear in the early Jurassic period. These dinosaurs had bony plates on their backs for protection against the large carnivorous dinosaurs that had evolved by this period. Their hind legs were longer than their forelegs, suggesting that they were descended from bipedal dinosaurs and had reverted to moving around on 4 legs in response to the increasing weight of the skeleton with its bony armor.

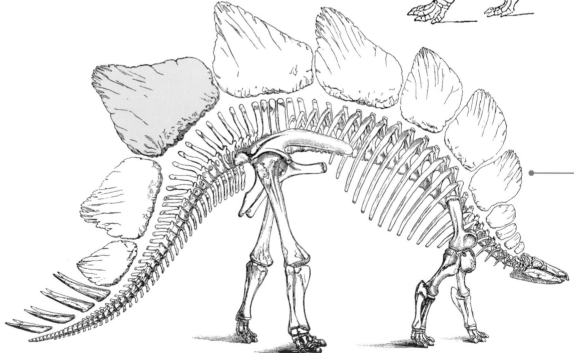

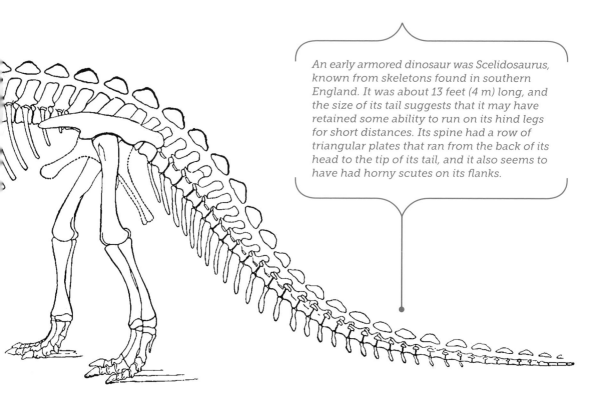

An early armored dinosaur was Scelidosaurus, known from skeletons found in southern England. It was about 13 feet (4 m) long, and the size of its tail suggests that it may have retained some ability to run on its hind legs for short distances. Its spine had a row of triangular plates that ran from the back of its head to the tip of its tail, and it also seems to have had horny scutes on its flanks.

Probably the most distinctive armored dinosaur is Stegosaurus from the late Jurassic period, with its double row of plates along an enormous arched backbone. The plates undoubtedly would have deterred predators, but the presence of branching grooves in the surface of the bones suggests that they may also have had a system of blood vessels close under the skin. This would have allowed the plates to be used as thermoregulators, with the large surface area being used to cool a large volume of blood to prevent the animal from overheating.

ANKYLOSAURS

By the early Cretaceous period the stegosaurs were largely extinct, with their place being taken by the ankylosaurs. These armored dinosaurs had bony plates on their backs that formed a kind of protective shell, and also bony spikes on their flanks for defense. Acanthopholis was described by the famous nineteenth-century biologist Thomas Henry Huxley on the basis of fossil remains found in southern England, and was one of the first ankylosaurs to be identified. It was about 16 feet (5 m) long, and its back was covered with oval, bony scutes. It also had protective spikes on its neck and shoulders.

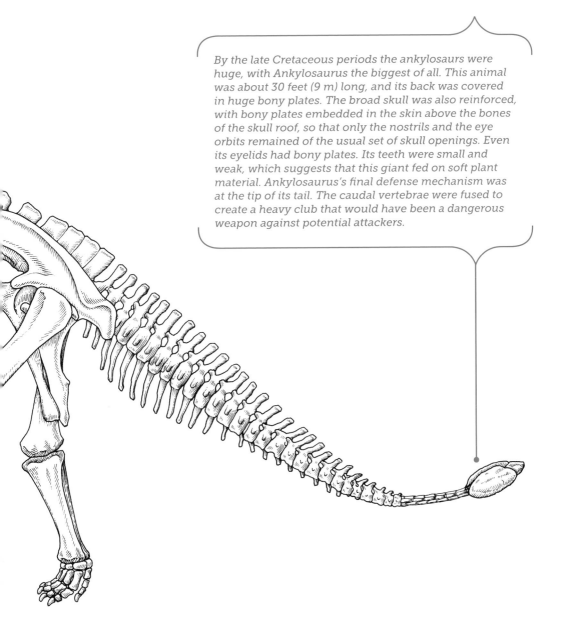

By the late Cretaceous periods the ankylosaurs were huge, with Ankylosaurus the biggest of all. This animal was about 30 feet (9 m) long, and its back was covered in huge bony plates. The broad skull was also reinforced, with bony plates embedded in the skin above the bones of the skull roof, so that only the nostrils and the eye orbits remained of the usual set of skull openings. Even its eyelids had bony plates. Its teeth were small and weak, which suggests that this giant fed on soft plant material. Ankylosaurus's final defense mechanism was at the tip of its tail. The caudal vertebrae were fused to create a heavy club that would have been a dangerous weapon against potential attackers.

HORNS &
BONEHEADS

The ceratopsia were the last of the dinosaurs to evolve in the late Cretaceous period, so their history was brief compared to the other dinosaurs. They had rather pointed skulls with long beaked snouts and horns, from which they get their name, "horn-faces." They evolved into huge dinosaurs, the best-known of which is Triceratops, but the first ceratopsia, like Protoceratops, below, were about the size of a cow. Protoceratops had the characteristic beak but only the beginnings of a horn on its snout. It also had a bony frill at the back of its skull, which is common to all the ceratopsia. This was primarily for the attachment of the jaw muscles, but it probably also functioned as a protective shield for the neck, and the size of the frills of later species suggests that it was also used for display, perhaps to attract mates.

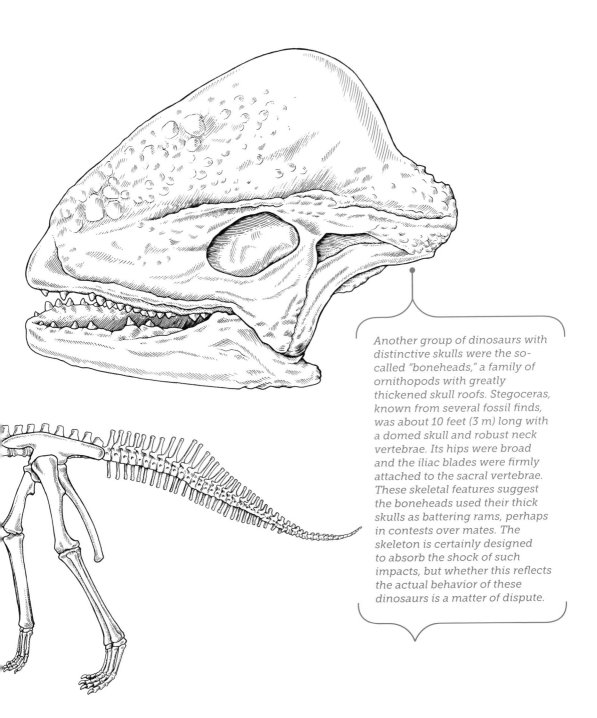

Another group of dinosaurs with distinctive skulls were the so-called "boneheads," a family of ornithopods with greatly thickened skull roofs. Stegoceras, known from several fossil finds, was about 10 feet (3 m) long with a domed skull and robust neck vertebrae. Its hips were broad and the iliac blades were firmly attached to the sacral vertebrae. These skeletal features suggest the boneheads used their thick skulls as battering rams, perhaps in contests over mates. The skeleton is certainly designed to absorb the shock of such impacts, but whether this reflects the actual behavior of these dinosaurs is a matter of dispute.

ICHTHYOSAURS

Fossils of Ichthyosaurus have been found in large
numbers in sedimentary rocks from the Jurassic period,
and are representative of a group of specialized marine
reptiles that first appeared in middle Triassic times. By this
point in evolutionary history the reptiles had developed
to become entirely terrestrial, so the ichthyosaurs
were making the return journey to the sea from
which their ancestors had emerged millions
of years before.

Ichthyosaurus was highly specialized for life in the ocean. It had a
long pointed skull which could cut through the water, and the back
of the skull connected to the spine in a streamlined sweep with no
real neck to speak of. Its jaws had rows of sharp teeth, and the large
eye sockets indicate its reliance on vision for hunting prey. Its
nostrils were on the top of its head to facilitate breathing.

The spine of the Ichthyosaurus bent downward at the tip to form the base of the tail fin, and the bones of the pelvis, shoulders, and legs were short and robust.

It had six or seven digits on each limb, and these were made up of a large number of flattened hexagonal bones that created wide, flat paddles. These would be used for steering while the ichthyosaur propelled itself by rhythmic sweeps of its muscular spine. Ichthyosaurus resembled modern porpoises and dolphins, and was likely to have been a fast and efficient hunter.

PLESIOSAURS

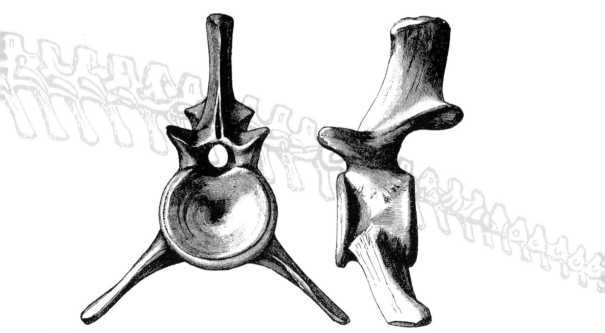

Another group of marine reptiles were the plesiosaurs, which flourished from late Triassic times to the end of the Cretaceous period. These animals showed a type of adaptation to life in the sea different from that of the ichthyosaurs. They were more similar in shape to modern seals, though many were much bigger. Plesiosaurus was the first of these reptiles to be discovered, in the early nineteenth century, and thus has given its name to the entire family. It was about 12 feet (3.5 m) long, about half of which was its long neck, made up of as many as 40 cervical vertebrae. The vertebrae, below, had long spines to attach the strong back and neck muscles.

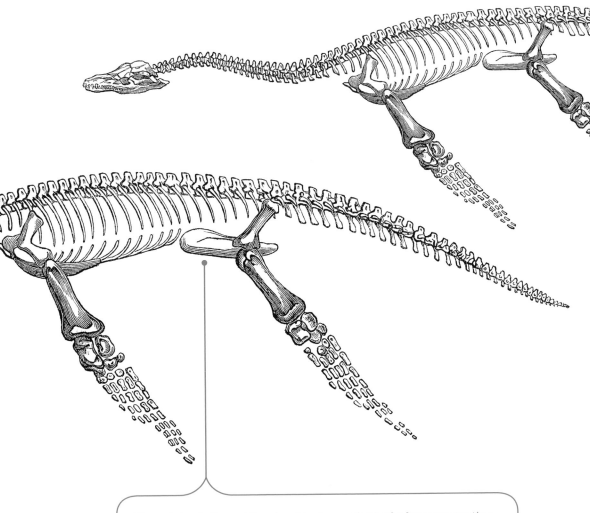

The pelvic girdle and the shoulder bones formed a large proportion of the animal's lower body, giving a firm base for the swimming muscles. The upper limb bones were long and robust for the attachment of these muscles, while the lower bones and the bones of the ankle and wrist were quite short. There were five digits on each limb, made up of as many as 20 cylindrical bones that formed very long, wide paddles. These would have been used like oars to propel the animal through the water, and it is likely that some plesiosaurs would also have been able to walk on land. Plesiosaurus had a relatively small skull with sharp, fish-catching teeth, though other species had shorter necks and much bigger heads.

PLATYPUS

The platypus belongs to a group of animals known as the monotremes whose
only other members are the echidnas. These animals offer a glimpse of the
prehistoric age of animal development that occurred between the mammal-like
reptiles and the emergence of true mammals. Monotremes are confined to New
Guinea and Australia, which for a long geological period was entirely separate
from the other land masses, so that its very specific fauna of marsupial animals
continued longer than was the case elsewhere, where the more developed
mammals prevailed.

*The skull of the platypus is
flattened and widened into a
ducklike bill, with the nostrils
on top of the snout. Although
the animal is born with three
teeth in each jaw, it loses
these soon after weaning. Its
eye and ear openings are at
the base of the skull; unlike
most mammals the platypus
has no external ears.*

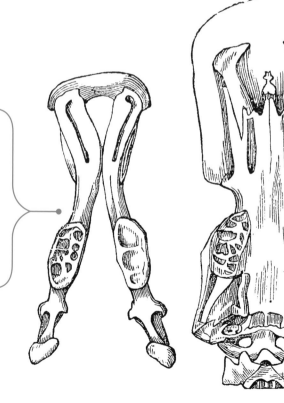

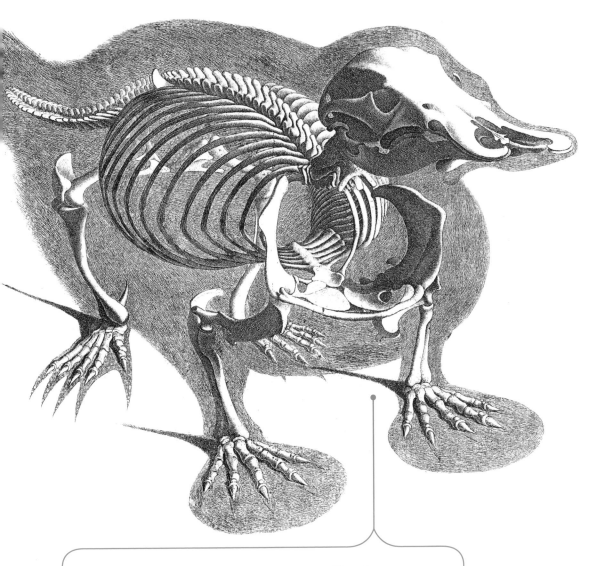

The skeleton of the platypus shows some reptilian elements, particularly the shoulder girdle, which has large coracoid bones and an interclavicle, an extra bone between the collar bones, both of which are characteristic of reptiles and birds but have been suppressed in mammals. The platypus has a reptilian gait, with the legs sticking out from the body rather than being directly underneath. It uses its front feet when swimming, with the back feet and tail used for steering. A notable feature of its skeleton is the sharp bony spur on the rear ankles which in the male platypus delivers a venom powerful enough to kill small animals.

PROBOSCIDS

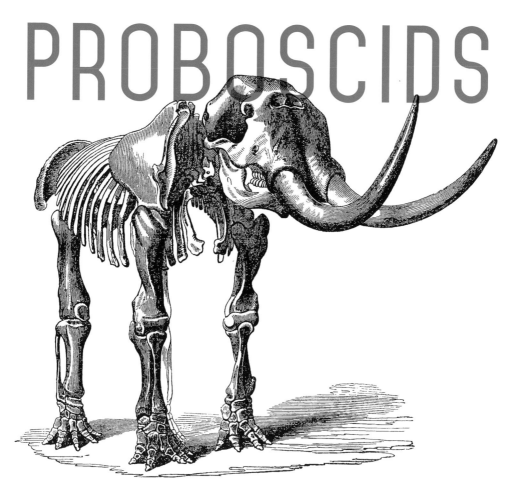

The Proboscidea were the ancestors of modern elephants, and though there are now only two species of these animals, in the Cenozoic era there were numerous different branches of the family. The mastodons were squat, heavy animals, not as tall as modern elephants, which lived in the Quaternary period. They had large tusks and trunks and distinctively cusped molars, from which the name derives, mastodon meaning "breast-tooth." The later mammoths had larger teeth with a greater number of crests, much like the teeth of modern elephants. Accommodating these large teeth was a problem that was solved by having them erupt only one or two at a time, with further teeth emerging from the jaw as the first wore down.

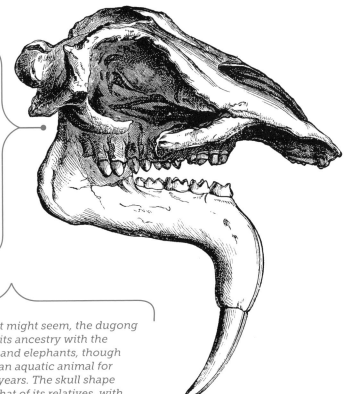

Deinotherium represented a side-branch of the Proboscidea which flourished from the late Tertiary period to the Quaternary. It had a flatter, lower skull than the mastodons, and the large nasal cavity suggests that it had a large strong trunk. Unlike the mastodons it had downward-pointing tusks in its lower jaw, which may have been used for digging up roots for food.

Strange as it might seem, the dugong also shares its ancestry with the mastodons and elephants, though it has been an aquatic animal for millions of years. The skull shape resembles that of its relatives, with a beaklike projection at the front and cheek teeth with the same pattern of front teeth being replaced by the back teeth pushing forward.

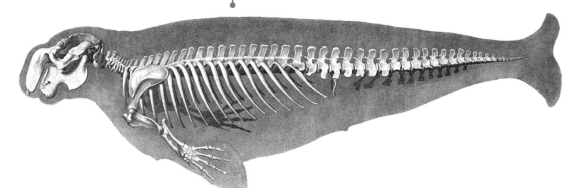

MEGAFAUNA

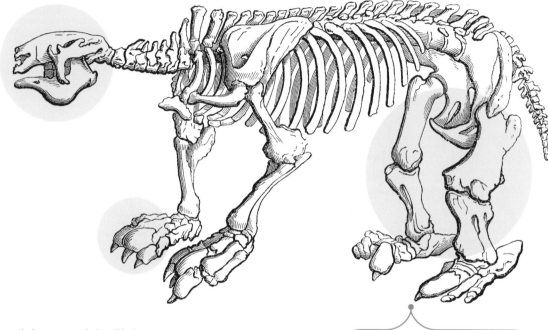

A feature of the Pleistocene epoch of the Quaternary was the prevalence of large animals, genera that we recognize today but with much larger species than now exist. This increase in size was a response to the change in climate, since the Pleistocene was the period known as the Ice Age, and a larger body size retains heat better than a smaller one. This is known as Bergmann's rule, after the zoologist who identified the phenomenon in the nineteenth century, and can be seen today in the fact that, broadly speaking, animals of the same genus increase in size the further away they live from the equator.

Megatherium was a large South American ground sloth, a relative of the modern tree sloths and anteaters, except that this animal was the size of an elephant. Its robust limbs, pelvis, and shoulder blades indicate its bulk. Fossilized footprints suggest that it may have walked on its hind legs. Certainly, it would have been able to raise itself up on its hind legs to reach up to tree branches.

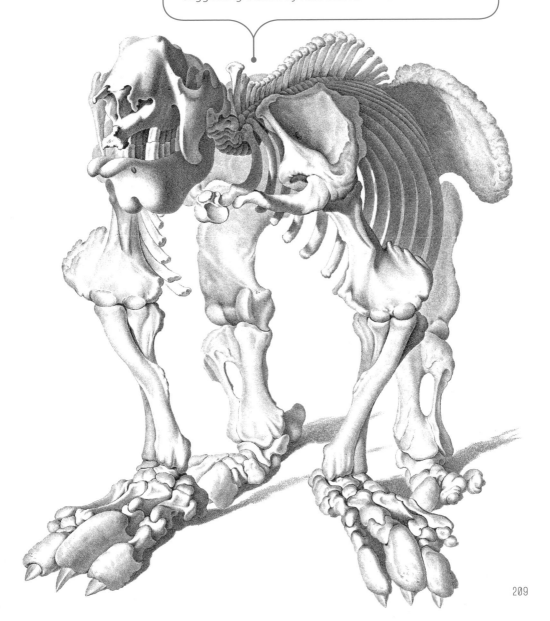

Megatherium had huge claws which were probably used for digging, but they may also have been used as offensive weapons for hunting. It had a large skull with heavy jaws and relatively unspecialized teeth, suggesting that it may have been omnivorous.

GIANT HERBIVORES

Although the largest mammals are now primarily located in Africa, in prehistoric times similar animals were widespread in Eurasia and the Americas. In the later Tertiary period camels appeared on the plains of North America, and enormous species gradually evolved that stood about 11 feet (3.3 m) tall at the shoulder. They had long limbs and tall upright processes on the spine, indicating a substantial hump. They had two-toed hooved feet, which developed in later species into spreading, padded feet adapted for walking in soft sand. The North American camels migrated from their place of origin to Eurasia and Africa during the early Quaternary period, by which time they had largely evolved into their modern form. Like many other large animals, they became extinct in North America at the end of the Ice Age.

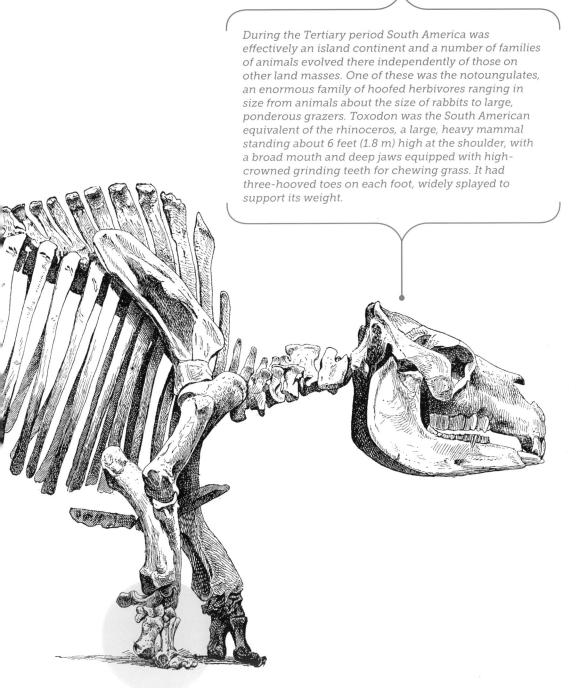

During the Tertiary period South America was effectively an island continent and a number of families of animals evolved there independently of those on other land masses. One of these was the notoungulates, an enormous family of hoofed herbivores ranging in size from animals about the size of rabbits to large, ponderous grazers. Toxodon was the South American equivalent of the rhinoceros, a large, heavy mammal standing about 6 feet (1.8 m) high at the shoulder, with a broad mouth and deep jaws equipped with high-crowned grinding teeth for chewing grass. It had three-hooved toes on each foot, widely splayed to support its weight.

AUSTRALASIA

Australia and New Zealand are unusual in terms of animal evolution since they were isolated from the other land masses from the beginning of the Tertiary period, so that their fauna developed in distinctive directions. The birds of New Zealand were the dominant animals in the absence of any mammalian competitors.

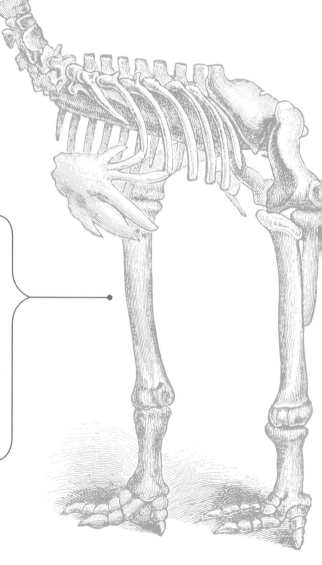

The giant flightless moa, Dinornis, was a tall browsing bird and could reach a height of about 12 feet (3.5 m). It had a robust skeleton with strong, solid leg and foot bones, powerful claws, and large hips. The wing structures have completely disappeared: there are no traces of coracoid or scapular bones, and the sternum lacks the keel that anchors the wing muscles in flying birds. When humans arrived in New Zealand around 700 years ago the moas had little defense. It is believed that they were hunted to extinction within about 100 years.

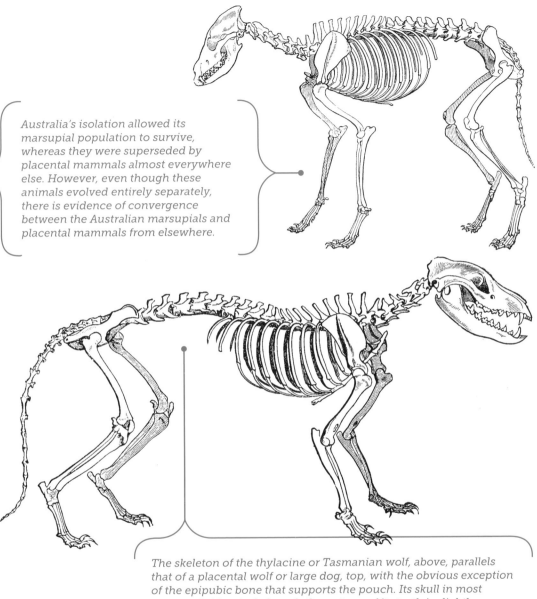

Australia's isolation allowed its marsupial population to survive, whereas they were superseded by placental mammals almost everywhere else. However, even though these animals evolved entirely separately, there is evidence of convergence between the Australian marsupials and placental mammals from elsewhere.

The skeleton of the thylacine or Tasmanian wolf, above, parallels that of a placental wolf or large dog, top, with the obvious exception of the epipubic bone that supports the pouch. Its skull in most respects is identical, though the pattern of its teeth is slightly different: the thylacine has molars with shearing and grinding surfaces, while these operations are performed by different teeth in a dog. Nonetheless, it is a good example of the way in which evolutionary developments arrive at the same end via different paths in responding to specific environmental demands.

GIANT CARNIVORES

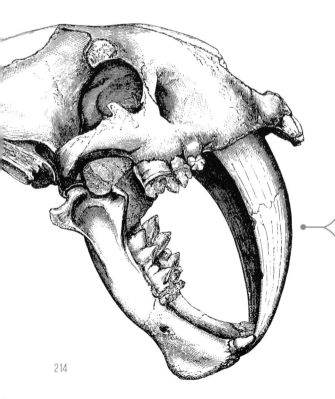

Just as the Ice Age herbivores grew larger in size, so the carnivores that ate them got bigger as well. Smilodon was a huge saber-toothed cat that stood about 4 feet (1.2 m) tall at the shoulder. Its powerful build and short tail indicate that it was an ambush predator rather than a runner.

> *The Smilodon's huge canines were oval in cross section and serrated along the rear edges. Its jaws had a wide gape, clearing the way for the long sabers to drive into the flesh of its prey with the full force of the heavy neck and shoulders behind them.*

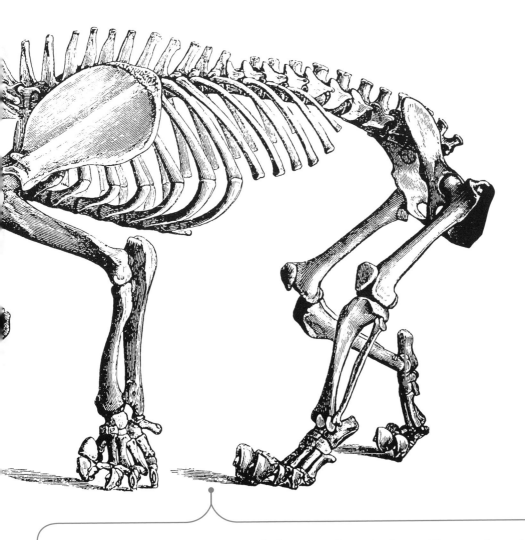

Smilodon was one of numerous animals that became extinct around 11,000 years ago, at about the time that humans first arrived in the Americas. It has been estimated that by 9000 BCE about two-thirds of the large mammal genera that had previously lived in North America had become extinct, including the mastodons, giant sloths, early giant horses and camels, and large rodents. The fact that this occurred over a relatively short period suggests that hunting was the main cause, with these large and slow-moving animals providing a ready source of meat. Climatic theories have also been advanced, but comparable extinctions of large animals did not occur in Africa and Eurasia, which had a longer history of human–animal interaction. This suggests that the sudden arrival of these efficient hunters in the Americas did not allow time for the animals to adapt to the new threat. And as the large, slow prey animals disappeared, so did the huge carnivores that preyed on them.

A DIRECTORY
OF SKELETONS

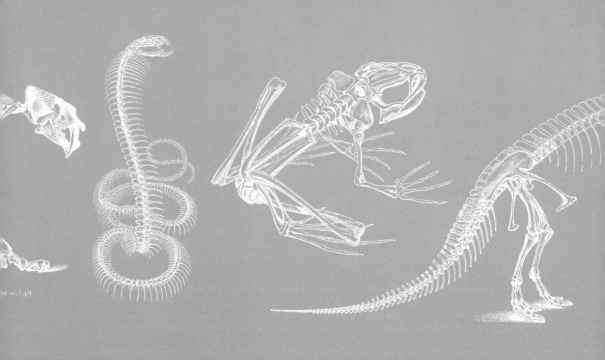

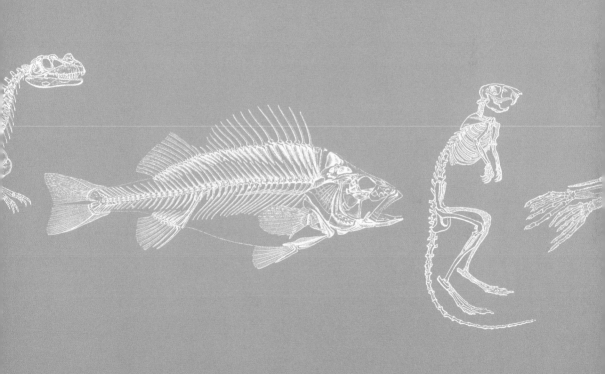

DIRECTORY

This directory gives some facts and figures and the family relationships of the animals whose skeletons feature in this book. It is organized in order of evolutionary development, from fish to mammals, and within each main section the skeletons are grouped together in their related taxonomic orders.

LAMPREY

CLASS	*Hyperoartia*
ORDER	*Petromyzontiformes*
SIZE	*5–40 inches (12–100 cm)*
RANGE	*temperate coastal and fresh waters worldwide*
DESCRIPTION	*38 species of jawless fish, some of which are parasitic carnivores, though many species do not feed as adults, living off reserves built up as larvae*

CHEIROLEPIS

CLASS	*Actinopterygii*
ORDER	*Cheirolepiformes*
FAMILY	*Cheirolepidae*
SIZE	*22 inches (56 cm)*
DESCRIPTION	*an extinct, predatory, freshwater fish that was fast swimming and probably hunted by sight*

EURYPHOLIS

CLASS	*Actinopterygii*
ORDER	*Ichthyodectiformes*
FAMILY	*Saurodontidae*
SIZE	*8 feet (2.5 m)*
DESCRIPTION	*a large, extinct, pelagic predator, much like a modern barracuda*

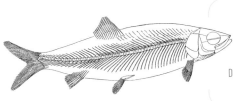

LEPTOLEPIS

CLASS	*Actinopterygii*
ORDER	*Leptolepiformes*
FAMILY	*Leptolepidae*
SIZE	*12 inches (30 cm)*
DESCRIPTION	*an extinct, pelagic fish that probably lived in schools, feeding off small invertebrates*

PERCH

CLASS	*Actinopterygii*
ORDER	*Perciformes*
FAMILY	*Percidae*
SIZE	*10–20 inches (25–50 cm)*
RANGE	*northern, central and eastern Europe, China, North America*
DESCRIPTION	*3 species of carnivorous, freshwater fish that feed on shellfish and insect larvae*

STURGEON

CLASS	*Actinopterygii*
ORDER	*Acipenseriformes*
FAMILY	*Acipenseridae*
SIZE	*7–12 feet (2–3.5 m)*
RANGE	*temperate coasts and lakes of Eurasia and North America*
DESCRIPTION	*27 species of bottom-feeding fish that eat crustacea and other small fish*

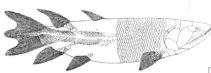

EUSTHENOPTERON

CLASS	*Sarcopterygii*
ORDER	*Osteolepidida*
FAMILY	*Tristichopteridae*
SIZE	*6 feet (1.8 m)*
DESCRIPTION	*an extinct, pelagic, lobe-finned predatory fish*

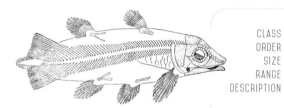

COELACANTH

CLASS	*Sarcopterygii*
ORDER	*Coelacanthiformes*
SIZE	*6–7 feet (1.8–2 m)*
RANGE	*East African coast, Indonesia*
DESCRIPTION	*a deep-sea, lobe-finned fish that feeds at night on small fish, octopus and squid*

NEOCERATODUS

CLASS	*Sarcopterygii*
ORDER	*Ceratodontiformes*
FAMILY	*Ceratodontidae*
SIZE	*3½–4 feet (1–1.2 m)*
RANGE	*Queensland, Australia*
DESCRIPTION	*a sedentary, nocturnal lungfish that lives in slow-moving rivers and pools, feeding on tadpoles, frogs, and small invertebrates*

CLADOSELACHE

CLASS	*Chondrichthyes*
ORDER	*Cladoselachiformes*
FAMILY	*Cladoselachidae*
SIZE	*6 feet (1.8 m)*
DESCRIPTION	*an extinct, fast-swimming shark that lived in the oceans off North America*

SKATE

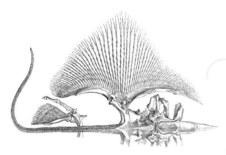

CLASS	*Chondrichthyes*
ORDER	*Rajiformes*
FAMILY	*Rajidae*
SIZE	*30 inches–8 feet (0.75–2.4 m)*
RANGE	*worldwide*
DESCRIPTION	*over 200 species of flat, mostly deep-sea fish that feed on small invertebrates and crustacea*

ICHTHYOSTEGA

CLASS	*Tetrapodomorpha*
ORDER	*Stegocephalia*
SIZE	*5 feet (1.5 m)*
DESCRIPTION	*an extinct, swamp-dwelling, carnivorous animal, transitional between fish and amphibians*

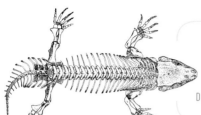

SEYMOURIA

CLASS	*Tetrapodomorpha*
ORDER	*Seymouriamorpha*
FAMILY	*Seymouriidae*
SIZE	*2 feet (60 cm)*
DESCRIPTION	*an extinct, chiefly terrestrial predatory amphibian*

FROG

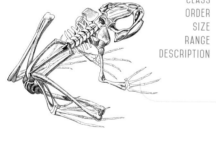

CLASS	*Amphibia*
ORDER	*Anura*
SIZE	*⅜–12 inches (1–30.5 cm)*
RANGE	*worldwide, concentrated in tropical rainforests*
DESCRIPTION	*4,800 species of mostly carnivorous amphibians, both arboreal and terrestrial, some of which are highly toxic*

ANCHISAURUS

CLASS	*Dinosauria*
ORDER	*Saurischia*
FAMILY	*Sauropodomorpha*
SIZE	*6–8 feet (1.8–2.4 m)*
DESCRIPTION	*a herbivorous, mostly bipedal dinosaur*

APATOSAURUS

CLASS	*Dinosauria*
ORDER	*Saurischia*
FAMILY	*Sauropodomorpha*
SIZE	*80 feet (24.4 m)*
DESCRIPTION	*a large, herbivorous, quadruped dinosaur that was formerly known as Brontosaurus*

CAMARASAURUS

CLASS	*Dinosauria*
ORDER	*Saurischia*
FAMILY	*Sauropodomorpha*
SIZE	*65 feet (20 m)*
DESCRIPTION	*a herbivorous quadruped with a characteristic box-shaped head*

DIPLODOCUS

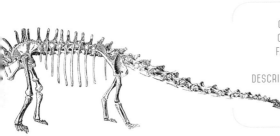

CLASS	*Dinosauria*
ORDER	*Saurischia*
FAMILY	*Sauropodomorpha*
SIZE	*90 feet (27.4 m)*
DESCRIPTION	*a long-necked, herbivorous quadruped whose tail was about twice the length of the neck and body combined*

COMPSOGNATHUS

CLASS	*Dinosauria*
ORDER	*Saurischia*
FAMILY	*Theropoda*
SIZE	*3 feet (0.9 m)*
DESCRIPTION	*a carnivorous, bipedal dinosaur about the size of a chicken, one of the first complete dinosaur skeletons ever found*

CERATOSAURUS

CLASS	*Dinosauria*
ORDER	*Saurischia*
FAMILY	*Theropoda*
SIZE	*17 feet (5 m)*
DESCRIPTION	*a carnivorous biped that may have hunted in packs*

TYRANNOSAURUS REX

CLASS	*Dinosauria*
ORDER	*Saurischia*
FAMILY	*Theropoda*
SIZE	*40 feet (12 m)*
DESCRIPTION	*a large, carnivorous predator with long, sharp teeth and an acute sense of smell*

IGUANADON

CLASS *Dinosauria*
ORDER *Ornithischia*
FAMILY *Iguanadontidae*
SIZE *20–30 feet (6–9 m)*
DESCRIPTION *a herbivorous, beaked dinosaur that was origi-*
nally thought to have been a quadruped, then was
reclassified as a biped, and is now thought once
again to have been a quadruped

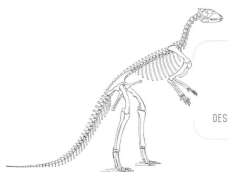

HYPSILOPHODON

CLASS *Dinosauria*
ORDER *Ornithischia*
FAMILY *Hypsilophodontidae*
SIZE *7–8 feet (2–2.4 m)*
DESCRIPTION *a fast-running, long-legged, bipedal herbivore*

CLAOSAURUS

CLASS *Dinosauria*
ORDER *Ornithischia*
FAMILY *Hadrosauridae*
SIZE *11–12 feet (3.3–3.7 m)*
DESCRIPTION *a relatively primitive member of the hadrosaurid*
family, a quadruped herbivore

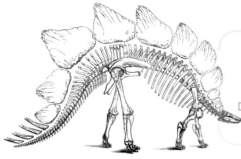

STEGOSAURUS

CLASS	*Dinosauria*
ORDER	*Ornithischia*
FAMILY	*Stegosauria*
SIZE	*30 feet (9 m)*
DESCRIPTION	*a large, browsing herbivore which had the smallest brain relative to its bulk of any dinosaur*

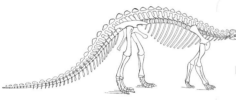

SCELIDOSAURUS

CLASS	*Dinosauria*
ORDER	*Ornithischia*
FAMILY	*Ankylosauria*
SIZE	*12 feet (3.7 m)*
DESCRIPTION	*a browsing, armored quadruped, which may have been able to run on its hind legs for short distances*

ANKYLOSAURUS

CLASS	*Dinosauria*
ORDER	*Ornithischia*
FAMILY	*Ankylosauria*
SIZE	*36 feet (11 m)*
DESCRIPTION	*a large herbivorous, quadruped, the largest and last of the ankylosaurs*

PROTOCERATOPS

CLASS   *Dinosauria*
ORDER   *Ornithischia*
FAMILY   *Ceratopsia*
SIZE   *8 feet (2.4 m)*
DESCRIPTION *an early, horn-headed, browsing animal that
            probably lived in large herds*

TRICERATOPS

CLASS   *Dinosauria*
ORDER   *Ornithischia*
FAMILY   *Ceratopsia*
SIZE   *30 feet (9 m)*
DESCRIPTION *the largest of the horned dinosaurs, with three
            horns and powerful beaked jaws*

PTERODACTYLUS

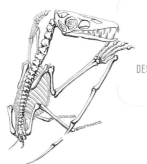

CLASS   *Reptilia*
ORDER   *Pterosauria*
FAMILY   *Pterodactylidae*
SIZE   *6 feet (1.8 m) wingspan*
DESCRIPTION *a flying, fish-eating reptile with a crested skull and
            a long beak*

ICHTHYOSAURUS

CLASS   *Reptilia*
ORDER   *Ichthyosauria*
FAMILY   *Ichthyosauridae*
SIZE   *6 feet (1.8 m)*
DESCRIPTION *a dolphin-shaped predator with long jaws and two pairs of ventral fins*

PLESIOSAURUS

CLASS   *Reptilia*
ORDER   *Plesiosauria*
FAMILY   *Plesiosauridae*
SIZE   *11 feet (3.3 m)*
DESCRIPTION *an aquatic predator that swam with a flying action, like a penguin*

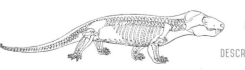

CYNOGNATHUS

CLASS   *Reptilia*
ORDER   *Therapsida*
FAMILY   *Cynodontidae*
SIZE   *3 feet (0.9 m)*
DESCRIPTION *an extinct, dog-like, carnivorous hunter whose fossil remains have been found worldwide*

ALLIGATOR

CLASS	*Reptilia*
ORDER	*Crocodilia*
FAMILY	*Alligatoridae*
SIZE	*8–13 feet (2.4–4 m)*
RANGE	*southeastern USA, China*
DESCRIPTION	*2 species of large, carnivorous reptiles that live in rivers and swampland*

COBRA

CLASS	*Reptilia*
ORDER	*Squamata*
FAMILY	*Elapidae*
SIZE	*6 inches–18 feet (15 cm–5.5 m)*
RANGE	*tropical and subtropical regions worldwide*
DESCRIPTION	*more than 300 species of fanged venomous snakes with distinctive neck shields*

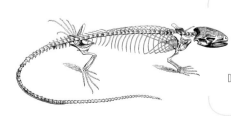

LIZARD

CLASS	*Reptilia*
ORDER	*Squamata*
FAMILY	*Lacertilia*
SIZE	*1½ inches–9 feet (4 cm–2.75 m)*
RANGE	*worldwide except Antarctica*
DESCRIPTION	*6,000 species of scaly, quadruped reptiles, making up about 60 percent of all reptile species*

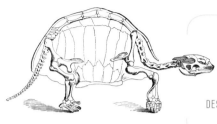

TORTOISE

CLASS	*Reptilia*
ORDER	*Testudines*
FAMILY	*Testudinidae*
SIZE	*3 inches–6 feet (7.5 cm–1.8 m)*
RANGE	*worldwide from temperate through tropical zones*
DESCRIPTION	*hard-shelled, herbivorous quadrupeds, known for their longevity*

TURTLE

CLASS	*Reptilia*
ORDER	*Testudines*
FAMILY	*Testudinidae*
SIZE	*3 inches–6 feet (7.5 cm–1.8 m)*
RANGE	*worldwide from temperate through tropical zones*
DESCRIPTION	*there are both freshwater and seawater species, and their diet includes invertebrates, fish and marine plants*

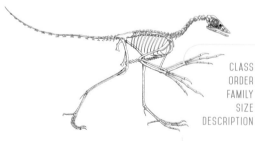

ARCHAEOPTERYX

CLASS	*Dinosauria*
ORDER	*Saurischia*
FAMILY	*Theropoda*
SIZE	*18 inches (45 cm)*
DESCRIPTION	*a feathered, flying dinosaur, a transitional animal between dinosaurs and birds*

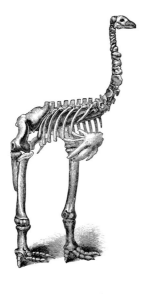

CLASS	*Aves*
ORDER	*Dinornithiformes*
FAMILY	*Dinornithidae*
SIZE	*12 feet (3.7 m)*
RANGE	*New Zealand*
DESCRIPTION	*an extinct, flightless bird, possibly the tallest bird there has ever been*

RHEA

CLASS	*Aves*
ORDER	*Rheiformes*
FAMILY	*Rheidae*
SIZE	*5½ feet (1.6 m)*
RANGE	*South America*
DESCRIPTION	*2 species of large, gray-plumaged, flightless birds that eat leaves, fruit, and seeds*

OSTRICH

CLASS	*Aves*
ORDER	*Struthioniformes*
FAMILY	*Struthionidae*
SIZE	*6–9 feet (1.8–2.75 m)*
RANGE	*grassland areas of northern, east, and southern Africa*
DESCRIPTION	*a black-and-white, very fast-running flightless bird, the largest living bird species*

CLASS   *Aves*
ORDER   *Anseriformes*
FAMILY   *Anatidae*
SIZE   *15–28 inches (38–70 cm)*
RANGE   *worldwide*
DESCRIPTION *a large number of species of waterbirds, many of which have bright plumage*

CLASS   *Aves*
ORDER   *Anseriformes*
FAMILY   *Anatidae*
SIZE   *40–55 inches (1–1.4 m)*
RANGE   *temperate zones worldwide*
DESCRIPTION *six species of large waterbirds, most of which have white plumage, and are known to mate for life*

CLASS   *Aves*
ORDER   *Phoenicopteriformes*
FAMILY   *Phoenicopteridae*
SIZE   *31–65 inches (80–165 cm) tall*
RANGE   *Central America, Andean South America, coastal Africa and SW Asia*
DESCRIPTION *six species of pinkish-reddish wading birds that live in enormous colonies of several thousand individuals*

PENGUIN

CLASS	*Aves*
ORDER	*Sphenisciformes*
FAMILY	*Spheniscidae*
SIZE	*16–40 inches (0.4–1 m)*
RANGE	*Antarctica, southern Australia, South America*
DESCRIPTION	*18 species of flightless birds with an upright stance and excellent swimming abilities*

TROPICAL SCREECH OWL

CLASS	*Aves*
ORDER	*Strigiformes*
FAMILY	*Strigidae*
SIZE	*7–9 inches (18–23 cm)*
RANGE	*South America*
DESCRIPTION	*a gray-brown or rufous arboreal bird that feeds on insects and small vertebrates*

BARN OWL

CLASS	*Aves*
ORDER	*Strigiformes*
FAMILY	*Tytonidae*
SIZE	*13–15 inches (33–38 cm)*
RANGE	*worldwide*
DESCRIPTION	*5 species of mostly nocturnal predators, with distinctive, heart-shaped pale faces*

CLASS	*Aves*
ORDER	*Falconiformes*
FAMILY	*Falconidae*
SIZE	*7–22 inches (18–56 cm)*
RANGE	*worldwide*
DESCRIPTION	*37 species of fast-flying, highly maneuvrable predatory birds*

CHICKEN

CLASS	*Aves*
ORDER	*Galliformes*
FAMILY	*Phasianidae*
SIZE	*11–17 inches (28–43 cm)*
RANGE	*worldwide*
DESCRIPTION	*a more or less flightless domesticated bird origi-nating in India, bred for millennia as a food source*

WOODPECKER

CLASS	*Aves*
ORDER	*Piciformes*
FAMILY	*Picidae*
SIZE	*5–22 inches (12.5–56 cm)*
RANGE	*worldwide except Australasia*
DESCRIPTION	*about 200 species of insectivorous, arboreal birds*

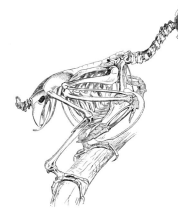

PARROT

CLASS	*Aves*
ORDER	*Psittaciformes*
SIZE	*3–36 inches (7.5–90 cm)*
RANGE	*tropical and subtropical regions worldwide*
DESCRIPTION	*nearly 400 species of brightly colored arboreal birds*

HUMMINGBIRD

CLASS	*Aves*
ORDER	*Apodiformes*
FAMILY	*Trochilidae*
SIZE	*3–5 inches (7.5–12.5 cm)*
RANGE	*temperate to tropical regions of the Americas*
DESCRIPTION	*338 species of small, brightly colored, nectar-eating birds*

PLATYPUS

CLASS	*Mammalia*
ORDER	*Monotremata*
FAMILY	*Ornithorhynchidae*
SIZE	*17–20 inches (43–50 cm)*
RANGE	*eastern Australia, Tasmania*
DESCRIPTION	*a thick-furred, semiaquatic animal that feeds on worms, insect larvae, and crustacea, one of only 5 species of egg-laying mammals*

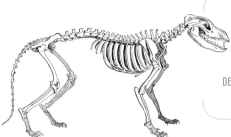

THYLACINE

CLASS   *Mammalia*
ORDER   *Dasyuromorphia*
FAMILY   *Thylacinidae*
SIZE   *40–50 inches (1–1.25 m)*
RANGE   *Australia, Tasmania, and New Guinea*
DESCRIPTION *a large carnivorous marsupial that became extinct early in the twentieth century*

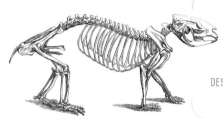

WOMBAT

CLASS   *Mammalia*
ORDER   *Diprotodontia*
FAMILY   *Vombatidae*
SIZE   *35–40 inches (0.9–1 m)*
RANGE   *Australia*
DESCRIPTION *3 species of short-legged, bulky, burrowing marsupials that feed on grasses, herbs, and roots*

KANGAROO

CLASS   *Mammalia*
ORDER   *Diprotodontia*
FAMILY   *Macropodidae*
SIZE   *4–6 feet (1.2–1.8 m)*
RANGE   *Australia*
DESCRIPTION *4 species of herbivorous marsupials, known for their ability to hop at speeds of up to 25 miles per hour*

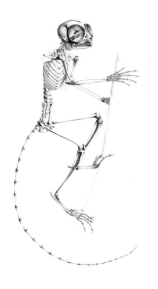

TARSIER

CLASS	*Mammalia*
ORDER	*Primates*
FAMILY	*Tarsiidae*
SIZE	*4–6 inches (10–15 cm)*
RANGE	*Southeast Asia*
DESCRIPTION	*10 species of arboreal, carnivorous, nocturnal animals, with long hind limbs and enormous eyes*

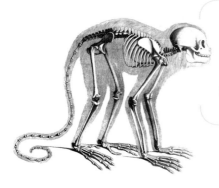

SPIDER MONKEY

CLASS	*Mammalia*
ORDER	*Primates*
FAMILY	*Atelidae*
SIZE	*20–22 inches (50–56 cm)*
RANGE	*Central America, northern South America*
DESCRIPTION	*7 species of long-limbed, agile, arboreal monkeys that eat fruit and nuts*

MACAQUE

CLASS	*Mammalia*
ORDER	*Primates*
FAMILY	*Cercopithecidae*
SIZE	*16–27 inches (40–68 cm)*
RANGE	*South Asia, North Africa, southern Europe*
DESCRIPTION	*23 species of mostly arboreal monkeys, the most widespread primate genus apart from humans*

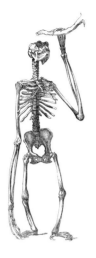

GIBBON

CLASS	*Mammalia*
ORDER	*Primates*
FAMILY	*Hylobatidae*
SIZE	*17–30 inches (43–76 cm)*
RANGE	*South and Southeast Asia*
DESCRIPTION	*16 species of mainly fruit-eating, arboreal apes which are able to swing at great speeds from branch to branch*

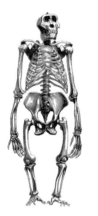

GORILLA

CLASS	*Mammalia*
ORDER	*Primates*
FAMILY	*Hominidae*
SIZE	*4–6 feet tall (1.2–1.8 m)*
RANGE	*central West Africa, Uganda, Democratic Republic of Congo*
DESCRIPTION	*2 species of ground-dwelling, mostly herbivorous apes, the largest extant primates*

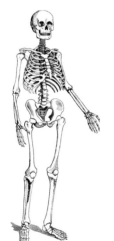

HUMAN

CLASS	*Mammalia*
ORDER	*Primates*
FAMILY	*Hominidae*
SIZE	*5–6½ feet tall (1.5–1.9 m)*
RANGE	*worldwide*
DESCRIPTION	*a species of primates characterized by bipedal locomotion, well-developed brains and highly complex societies*

CLASS	Mammalia
ORDER	Eulipotyphia
FAMILY	Soricidae
SIZE	4 inches (10 cm)
RANGE	Europe, Central Asia
DESCRIPTION	a thick-furred, grayish-black carnivore, one of the few venomous mammals

CLASS	Mammalia
ORDER	Eulipotyphia
FAMILY	Erinaceidae
SIZE	4–6 inches (10–15 cm)
RANGE	Europe, Asia, North Africa
DESCRIPTION	17 species of spiny, nocturnal omnivores, known for their ability to roll into a ball for defense

CLASS	Mammalia
ORDER	Eulipotyphia
FAMILY	Talpidae
SIZE	1–8 inches (2.5–20 cm)
RANGE	Europe, North America, southern Asia
DESCRIPTION	46 species of dark-furred, cylinder-shaped car-nivores, most of which are subterranean, though some species are aquatic

CLASS	Mammalia
ORDER	Chiroptera
SIZE	6–65 inches (15–165 cm) wingspan
RANGE	worldwide
DESCRIPTION	1,240 species of mostly carnivorous flying mammals, the second largest mammalian order after the rodents

MASTODON

CLASS	Mammalia
ORDER	Proboscidea
FAMILY	Mammutidae
SIZE	7–10 feet (2–3 m) tall, 11–13 feet (3.3–4 m) long
RANGE	North and Central America
DESCRIPTION	an extinct, forest-dwelling, herd animal, with the appearance of a short-legged elephant

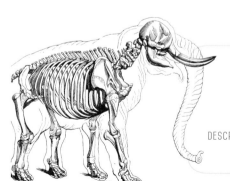

AFRICAN ELEPHANT

CLASS	Mammalia
ORDER	Proboscidea
FAMILY	Elephantidae
SIZE	11–13 feet (3.3–4 m) tall
RANGE	central, eastern, and southern Africa
DESCRIPTION	1 of 2 species of herbivorous, herding animals, the largest extant land-dwelling animal

DUGONG

CLASS	*Mammalia*
ORDER	*Sirenia*
FAMILY	*Dugongidae*
SIZE	*8–10 feet (2.4–3 m)*
RANGE	*Australasia, eastern Africa*
DESCRIPTION	*a seal-shaped, marine herbivore found in warm coastal waters*

MEGATHERIUM

CLASS	*Mammalia*
ORDER	*Pilosa*
FAMILY	*Megatheriidae*
SIZE	*20 feet (6 m) long*
RANGE	*South America*
DESCRIPTION	*6 species of extinct, herbivorous ground sloths that lived in temperate grasslands and woodlands*

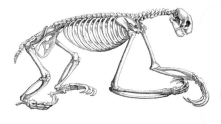

THREE-TOED SLOTH

CLASS	*Mammalia*
ORDER	*Pilosa*
FAMILY	*Bradypodidae*
SIZE	*18 inches (46 cm)*
RANGE	*Central America, northern South America*
DESCRIPTION	*4 species of arboreal, shaggy, extremely slow-moving herbivores*

ANTEATER

CLASS	*Mammalia*
ORDER	*Pilosa*
FAMILY	*Vermilingua*
SIZE	*14–70 inches (35 cm–1.8 m)*
RANGE	*Central America, northern South America*
DESCRIPTION	*4 species of insectivorous animals with elongated snouts and long tongues*

ARMADILLO

CLASS	*Mammalia*
ORDER	*Cingulata*
FAMILY	*Chlamyphoridae/Dasypodidae*
SIZE	*6–55 inches (15cm–1.4 m)*
RANGE	*South America, Central America, southern USA*
DESCRIPTION	*21 species of insectivorous animals with thick, leathery carapaces and strong digging claws*

GIRAFFE

CLASS	*Mammalia*
ORDER	*Artiodactyla*
FAMILY	*Giraffidae*
SIZE	*14–18 feet (4.25–5.5 m) tall*
RANGE	*central, eastern, and southern Africa*
DESCRIPTION	*a ruminant herbivore, the tallest extant land animal*

HIPPOPOTAMUS

CLASS   *Mammalia*
ORDER   *Artiodactyla*
FAMILY   *Hippopotamidae*
SIZE   *5 feet (1.5 m) tall, 10–15 feet (3–4.5 m) long*
RANGE   *eastern Sub-Saharan Africa*
DESCRIPTION *a large, semiaquatic, barrel-shaped, highly aggressive herbivore*

GREENLAND WHALE

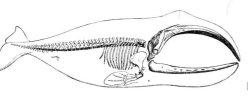

CLASS   *Mammalia*
ORDER   *Cetacea*
FAMILY   *Balaenidae*
SIZE   *40–45 feet (12–13.7 m)*
RANGE   *Arctic and sub-Arctic oceans*
DESCRIPTION *1 of the 15 species of the baleen whale suborder that filter feed on plankton and small crustacea*

SPERM WHALE

CLASS   *Mammalia*
ORDER   *Cetacea*
FAMILY   *Odontoceti*
SIZE   *50–60 feet (15.25–18.25 m)*
RANGE   *worldwide*
DESCRIPTION *1 of 27 species of the toothed whale suborder, which includes beaked whales, narwhals, and belugas, which use echolocation to find prey and navigate in deep water*

DOLPHIN

CLASS	*Mammalia*
ORDER	*Cetacea*
FAMILY	*Delphinidae/Iniidae/Platanistidae/Pontoporiidae*
SIZE	*5–30 feet (1.5–9 m)*
RANGE	*worldwide*
DESCRIPTION	*40 species of carnivorous, marine mammals, many of which are fast swimmers and all of which have highly developed hearing*

TOXODON

CLASS	*Mammalia*
ORDER	*Notoungulata*
FAMILY	*Toxodontidae*
SIZE	*8–9 feet long (2.4–2.75 m)*
RANGE	*South America*
DESCRIPTION	*a large, extinct, hoofed herbivore, similar to a rhinoceros*

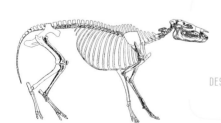

HYRACOTHERIUM

CLASS	*Mammalia*
ORDER	*Perissodactyla*
FAMILY	*Palaeotheriidae*
SIZE	*22–25 inches (56–64 cm) long, 8–14 inches (20–36 cm) tall*
DESCRIPTION	*an extinct, browsing, hoofed herbivore, an ancestor of the modern horse*

HORSE

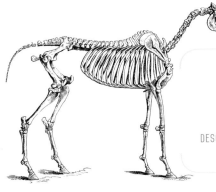

CLASS	*Mammalia*
ORDER	*Perissodactyla*
FAMILY	*Equidae*
SIZE	*30–70 inches (0.75–1.8 m) tall*
RANGE	*worldwide*
DESCRIPTION	*1 of 7 species of single-hoofed herbivores, which include zebras and donkeys*

RHINO

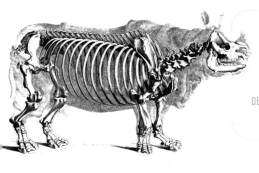

CLASS	*Mammalia*
ORDER	*Perissodactyla*
FAMILY	*Rhinocerotidae*
SIZE	*4–6 feet (1.2–1.8 m) tall, 8–15 feet (2.4–4.6 m) lo*
RANGE	*Central and Southern Africa, Southern Asia*
DESCRIPTION	*5 species of large, thick-skinned herbivores, 3 of which are in danger of extinction*

SEAL

CLASS	*Mammalia*
ORDER	*Carnivora*
FAMILY	*Pinnipedia*
SIZE	*3–26 feet (0.9–8 m)*
RANGE	*worldwide*
DESCRIPTION	*33 species of semiaquatic, marine carnivores, which include walruses and sea lions*

WOLF

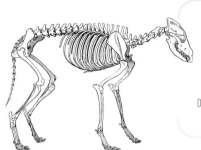

CLASS	*Mammalia*
ORDER	*Carnivora*
FAMILY	*Canidae*
SIZE	*32–34 inches (80–86 cm) tall, 40–60 inches (1–1.5 m) long*
RANGE	*North America, Eurasia*
DESCRIPTION	*a large, intelligent, and highly territorial carnivorous pack animal*

BOXER

CLASS	*Mammalia*
ORDER	*Carnivora*
FAMILY	*Canidae*
SIZE	*21–25 inches (53–63 cm) tall*
DESCRIPTION	*a short-haired dog with a broad, short muzzle*

DACHSHUND

CLASS	*Mammalia*
ORDER	*Carnivora*
FAMILY	*Canidae*
SIZE	*8–9 inches (20–23 cm) tall*
DESCRIPTION	*a short-legged, long-bodied dog bred to flush out burrow-dwelling prey animals*

SMILODON

CLASS	*Mammalia*
ORDER	*Carnivora*
FAMILY	*Felidae*
SIZE	*40–45 inches (100–115 cm) tall, 5–7 feet (1.5–2 m) long*
RANGE	*North and South America*
DESCRIPTION	*a robust, carnivorous cat with large saberlike canines*

LION

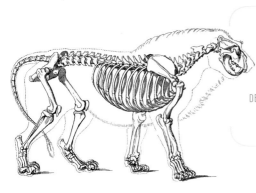

CLASS	*Mammalia*
ORDER	*Carnivora*
FAMILY	*Felidae*
SIZE	*5–8 feet (1.5–2.4 m)*
RANGE	*sub-Saharan Africa*
DESCRIPTION	*a species of large cat, second only in size to the tiger, known for living and hunting in large family groups*

POLAR BEAR

CLASS	*Mammalia*
ORDER	*Carnivora*
FAMILY	*Ursidae*
SIZE	*6–10 feet (1.8–3 m)*
RANGE	*Arctic Circle*
DESCRIPTION	*a large carnivore with thick white fur and a layer of insulating body fat*

DORMOUSE

CLASS	*Mammalia*
ORDER	*Rodentia*
FAMILY	*Gliridae*
SIZE	*2–7 inches (5–18 cm)*
RANGE	*Europe, Africa, Asia*
DESCRIPTION	*29 species of small, omnivorous, mostly arboreal rodents, temperate species of which hibernate*

BEAVER

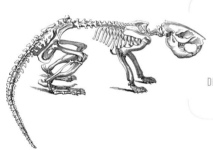

CLASS	*Mammalia*
ORDER	*Rodentia*
FAMILY	*Castoridae*
SIZE	*30–35 inches (75–90 cm)*
RANGE	*Europe, North America*
DESCRIPTION	*2 species of semiaquatic, herbivorous rodents known for building timber dams and lodges*

JERBOA

CLASS	*Mammalia*
ORDER	*Rodentia*
FAMILY	*Dipodidae*
SIZE	*2–6 inches (5–15 cm)*
RANGE	*northern Africa, Central Asia, northern China*
DESCRIPTION	*33 species of nocturnal, hopping, desert rodents*

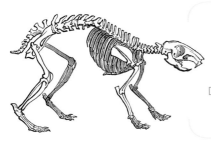

CLASS   *Mammalia*
ORDER   *Rodentia*
FAMILY   *Dasyproctidae*
SIZE   *17–25 inches (43–63 cm)*
RANGE   *Central America, northern South America*
DESCRIPTION *11 species of rodents that eat fruit, roots, and nuts,*
            and can live for up to 20 years, much longer than
            most rodents

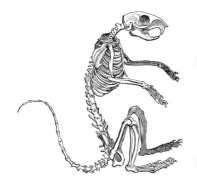

SQUIRREL

CLASS   *Mammalia*
ORDER   *Rodentia*
FAMILY   *Sciuridae*
SIZE   *3–25 inches (7.5–63 cm)*
DESCRIPTION *over 280 species of rodents, mostly thought of as*
            arboreal animals though the majority of species
            are ground-dwelling

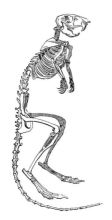

AFRICAN JUMPING HARE

CLASS   *Mammalia*
ORDER   *Rodentia*
FAMILY   *Pedetidae*
SIZE   *14–18 inches (35–45 cm*
RANGE   *southern Africa*
DESCRIPTION *a nocturnal, burrowing rodent that can leap*
            about 5 times its own body length

GLOSSARY

appendicular
Relating to the limbs, i.e., legs, arms, wings, or flippers.

arboreal
Living primarily or exclusively in trees.

canines
Two sharp, pointed teeth on either side of the upper and lower jaw, prominent in carnivores.

carnassials
Paired upper and lower premolars or molars with sharp edges that pass each other in a shearing motion, common to many carnivores.

carnivore
An animal that eats other animals, including insects, larvae, and crustacea.

cartilage
Flexible, fibrous, connective tissue that forms part of skeletal joints.

caudal
Relating to the lower end of the spine or the tail.

centrum
The solid section of a vertebra, from which the spinal processes and the neural arch project.

cervical
Relating to the upper end of the spine or the neck.

chitin
A structural polysaccharide that forms a composite material with proteins to form the exoskeleton of insects, and with calcium carbonate to form the shells of crustacea.

collagen
A structural protein, the main component of connective tissue.

coracoid
A bone that forms part of the shoulder assembly of non-mammalian vertebrates, connecting the scapula to the sternum.

distal
The end of a bone further away from the trunk of the body.

dorsal
Relating to or positioned on the back.

flange
A ridge or lip for the attachment of a muscle.

fontanel
A membranous gap between the bones of the skull in some animals that allows flexion during birth.

foramen magnum
The hole beneath the skull through which the spinal cord passes.

herbivore
An animal that eats vegetable matter, e.g., leaves, grasses, roots, nuts, fruit.

ilium
The upper part of the pelvis.

incisors
Narrow, edged teeth at the front of the upper and lower jaw.

ischium
The lower part of the pelvis.

keratin
A structural protein that forms tough body tissues such as nails, claws, feathers, beaks, scales, and horns.

lumbar
Relating to the lower part of the spine immediately before the tail.

mandible
The lower jaw.

marine
Relating to an animal that lives in the sea.

maxilla
The upper jaw.

molars
Large grinding teeth at the back of the upper and lower jaw.

morphology
The form and structure of an organism.

nares
The nostrils of a bird, usually located on the top of the beak.

neural arch
Hollow channel in a vertebra that carries the spinal cord.

omnivore
An animal that eats both animal and plant material.

operculum
A flap of bone or skin that covers a bodily aperture, e.g., the nares of a bird or the gills of a fish.

ornithopod
A member of the group of bipedal, ornithischian, grazing dinosaurs.

ossicles
The bones of the middle ear that transmit vibrations from the eardrum to the inner ear.

pectoral
Relating to or positioned on the chest.

pelagic
The region of a body of water that is neither near the shore nor near the bottom.

periosteum
A dense layer of connective tissue that covers the surface of a bone.

phalanges
Fingers and toes.

pneumatized
Of bones, having air sacs within.

process
A projection from a bone for the attachment of muscles.

proximal
The end of a bone that is nearer to the trunk of the body.

pygostyle
Structure formed by the fusing of the final caudal vertebrae of a bird to create a support for the musculature of the tail feathers.

scapula
The shoulder blade.

synsacrum
Structure formed by the fusing of the caudal vertebrae with the lower lumbar vertebrae, common to dinosaurs and birds.

terrestrial
Living primarily or exclusively on the ground.

theropod
A member of the group of bipedal, saurischian, carnivorous dinosaurs.

thoracic
Relating to the central part of the spine to which the ribs are usually attached.

ventral
Relating to or positioned on the belly.

GEOLOGICAL TIMELINE

The earth's origins can be dated to about 4,600 million years ago (mya), but as far as paleontology is concerned, the significant date is around 545 mya, when the fossil record begins. Geological time since then is divided into eras, periods, and epochs on the basis of the repeated patterns of distinctive fossils or fossil assemblages that are found in particular layers of the earth's surface. This timeline gives the date at which each period began.

CENOZOIC ERA

Quaternary Period
Holocene Epoch 0.01 mya
Pleistocene Epoch 1.8 mya

Tertiary Period
Pliocene Epoch 5.3 mya
Miocene Epoch 24 mya
Oligocene Epoch 34 mya
Eocene Epoch 56 mya
Paleocene Epoch 65 mya

MEZOZOIC ERA

Cretaceous Period 144 mya
Jurassic Period 200 mya
Triassic Period 251 mya

PALEOZOIC ERA

Permian Period 299 mya
Carboniferous Period 359 mya
Devonian Period 417 mya
Silurian Period 443 mya
Ordovician Period 495 mya
Cambrian Period 545 mya

PALEOZOIC ERA

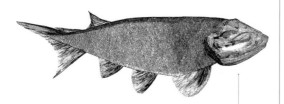

550 540 530 520 510 500 490 480 470 460 450 440 430 420 410 400 390 380 370 360 350 340 330 320 310 300 290 280 270 260 250

Devonian Period
417 mya

FURTHER READING

BOOKS

Benton, Michael J. *Vertebrate Paleontology*.
3rd ed. Oxford: Blackwell Publishing, 2005.

Bonner, John Tyler. *Why Size Matters*.
Princeton, NJ: Princeton University Press, 2006.

Colbert, Edwin H. *Evolution of the Vertebrates*.
3rd ed. New York: John Wiley, 1980.

Davies, Simon J. M. *The Archaeology of Animals*.
London: Batsford, 1987.

Dixon, Dougal. *The Complete Illustrated
Encyclopedia of Dinosaurs & Prehistoric
Creatures*. London: Anness Publishing, 2014.

Encyclopedia of Mammals. New York:
Marshall Cavendish, 1997.

Layman, Dale Pierre. *Anatomy Demystified*.
New York: McGraw Hill, 2004.

Mammal Anatomy: An Illustrated Guide.
New York: Marshall Cavendish, 2010.

Parker, Steve. *Skeleton*.
London: Dorling Kindersley, 2002.

Rackham, James. *Animal Bones*. London:
British Museum Press, 1994.

WEBSITES

www.tolweb.org/tree/phylogeny.html

www.edgeofexistence.org/index.php

www.ucl.ac.uk/museums-static/obl4he/
vertebratediversity/index.html

www.animals.nationalgeographic.com

www.rspb.org.uk

www.audubon.org/

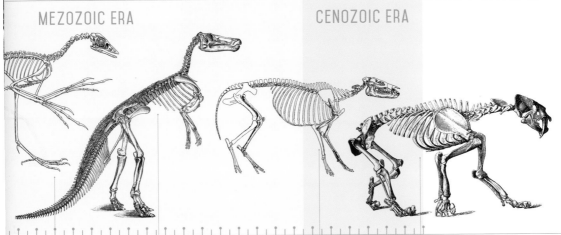

MEZOZOIC ERA

CENOZOIC ERA

220 210 200 190 180 170 160 150 140 130 120 110 100 90 80 70 60 50 40 30 20 10 0 million years ago

Cretaceous
Period
144 mya

Eocene Epoch
56 mya

Pleistocene
Epoch
1.8 mya

Jurassic Period 200 mya

INDEX

PICTURE CREDITS

The publisher would like to thank the following for permission to reproduce copyright material:

Sandra Pond 158–9 (bottom), 164–5 (left), 183 (both), 196–7, 198–9 (both); Shutterstock/Hein Nouwens 212.

Every effort has been made to trace copyright holders and to obtain their permission for the use of copyright material. The publisher apologizes for any errors or omissions in the list above and will gratefully incorporate any corrections in future reprints if notified.